WANLESS OF INDIA

LANCET OF THE LORD

SIR WILLIAM JAMES WANLESS, KT.

WANLESS OF INDIA

LANCET OF THE LORD

LILLIAN EMERY WANLESS

Illustrated by Beatrice Stevens

PUBLISHERS   W. A. WILDE COMPANY   BOSTON

WANLESS OF INDIA—LANCET
OF THE LORD

I write this story of the saintly surgeon
for the inspiration of the youth of today.

—L. E. W.

"The greatest satisfaction in life is found in service."

—WILLIAM WANLESS.

LIST OF ILLUSTRATIONS

Preface

This story dramatizes the life of a truly great man. It is based on fact. However, since fancy can create a background against which characters from real life may be set forth in clearer light and more distinct outline, this biography has been illumined by imagination.

The hero of this story is Sir William James Wanless, K.B., K.I.H., M.D., F.A.C.S., an internationally-known surgeon and distinguished Christian philanthropist.

Sir William, his family, and the Maharajah of Kolhapur are pictured according to life, but the other characters are fictitious. Imaginary conversations fill in around true events. The author, Lady Wanless, missionary colleague in India for twenty years, writes from personal knowledge, and has made this fictionized biography fascinating and inspiring. The setting is Miraj, India. This presentation will be better appreciated after a brief review of the main incidents in this extraordinary career.

William James Wanless was born May 1, 1865, at Charleston, a village near Toronto, Ontario, Canada. He was the son of John Wanless and Elizabeth Graham Wanless. Most of his life until manhood was

spent in the city of Toronto. In 1889, he was gradu-
ated from the Medical College of the University of
New York, New York, and the same year was sent to
India by the Foreign Board of the Presbyterian
Church in the United States of America

He was the first medical missionary sent to the
Western India Mission. Located at Sangli, 300 miles
southeast of Bombay, in a densely populated village
area, he obtained a thorough knowledge of village life.
Arriving with no equipment except a diploma and a
personal medicine case he began a lifework which
resulted in astonishing achievement.

After two years in Sangli, in which time the young
doctor had seen 15,000 patients, he moved to Miraj,
five miles distant, where he purchased land and built
his hospital. As the needs arose he continued to build.
The institutions of which Sir William Wanless was
the founder and manager are the following: a general
hospital, six branch hospitals, a convalescent home,
a medical college, a training school for nurses, a
leprosarium and a tuberculosis sanatorium. When
he retired, this medical center at Miraj was the
largest medical work under Christian auspices in all
India. He also started the Mary Wanless Memorial
Hospital at Kolhapur which was a gift from the
Maharajah of Kolhapur, in appreciation of medical
services rendered to him.

A secretary of the Foreign Board has said that this
is, no doubt, the "greatest piece of work by one man"
in the history of medical missions. Another secre-

tary said, " Any one of Dr. Wanless' three outstanding achievements was enough for one successful career—the hospital, the medical school, or the tuberculosis sanatorium."

It is a remarkable fact that more than three-fourths of the funds for building and maintaining these institutions were given by the people of India. Grateful patients came offering gifts of land, buildings, and money.

Many of the largest units of the hospital were individual gifts. It was the doctor's love for the people and his solicitude for their needs that led him to keep expanding the work to fill those needs. He did it on his own initiative and not for money or fame, but for love. His pleasant personality and selfless labors won the hearts of the people. A saying of his was: " The greatest satisfaction in life is found in service." " His versatile gifts and achievements were amazing and yet he had a spirit of real humility," writes a missionary. Patients who passed through just one of the institutions, the hospital, numbered over a million and a half at the time Sir William retired.

The Wanless Hospital was noted for its surgery. The doctor was always " first with the latest " in India in modern methods. Some of these were the use of X-Ray and radium, and nitrous-oxide-gas in anesthesia. He was the first surgeon in India to do the gastro-enterostomy operation. He was noted for his success in abdominal as well as ophthalmic sur-

gery. He performed 75,000 operations. He gave
sight to 13,000 blind. In the middle of his career, not
satisfied with the instruments then in vogue for the
extraction of the lens in cataract operations, he in-
vented an instrument and had it made by John Weiss
& Son, London, England, which the firm named
the "Wanless Extractor." In 1918, the doctor was
made a Fellow of the American College of Surgeons
(F.A.C.S.) in recognition of his record of successful
surgery.

Among the European patients, four hundred were
missionaries. Most of these cases were surgical, and
the record was one hundred per cent recoveries. One
of the patients, the well-known evangelist, the Rev.
E. Stanley Jones, D.D., says, "I went a thousand
miles in India to have Dr. Wanless operate on me, for
he was not only the outstanding surgeon of Asia, but
one of the greatest of the world, and more than all he
was a real Christian. That combination made him a
truly great man."

Perhaps one of the best deserved tributes paid was
by an ignorant, low-caste villager from North India,
who was asked, "Why did you pass by the many
large city hospitals and come to this one?" He
seemed surprised at the question and in simple faith
said, "Because the doctor prays before he operates."

When Dr. Wanless went to Miraj in 1892 there
were no Protestant Christians there. In a few
months, with the first converts, he organized a church,
which is the present Miraj church. Since the death

of Sir William, the Indian members organized the Wanless Memorial Band and it continues to carry on evangelistic work in the surrounding villages.

Wanless was a household word in India. It was said of the doctor that he was the best-loved foreigner in that country. The influence of his life upon the social and religious uplift of the people cannot be truly estimated. " Dr. Wanless was one of the giants of medical missions of which there has been no greater," comments Dr. E. M. Dodd, medical secretary of the Foreign Board.

The medical school he established in 1897 has continued through the years. In 1916 he succeeded in having his private school affiliated with the College of Physicians and Surgeons at Bombay, so that the students might receive degrees. This Miraj Medical College is the only medical school in India for training men under Christian auspices. Dr. Wanless used to say, " The most worthwhile part of my work is the training of Christian doctors for service to their fellow men." Thus his life was multiplied through the many graduates of the school who are to be found, not only on the Wanless hospital staff, but in all parts of India. The alumni maintain a Sir William Wanless scholarship.

In 1905, Dr. Wanless organized the Missionary Medical Association of India, now known as the Christian Medical Association. He was President for seventeen years, 1911–1928, and on retirement was made President-Emeritus.

The Presbyterian Church in the U. S. A. honored the doctor by sending him as a delegate to the World's Missionary Conference, held in Edinburgh, Scotland, 1910, as the sole representative of its Presbyterian foreign medical work.

While on furloughs, the doctor toured extensively, preaching and lecturing in behalf of foreign missions and the Student Volunteer Movement. He spoke in many colleges and universities and gained many recruits for the cause.

Sir William was a prolific writer for magazines, both in the fields of medicine and missions. For medical journals he wrote on surgery and tropical diseases, sharing with others the knowledge he had gained through his research and personal experiences. He also wrote numerous articles for religious magazines, and booklets with facts on foreign missions for young people. As an author, he wrote " Medical Missions " and a volume entitled " An American Doctor at Work in India." By invitation, he read a paper before the New York Academy of Medicine, New York City, in 1929, on " Medicine in India."

Sir William's last labor of love for India was founding the tuberculosis sanatorium. He purchased a tract of 105 acres one mile from the leprosarium and three miles from the central hospital and built several units of this large institution. It was named the Sir William Wanless Tuberculosis Sanatorium by its board of managers, following the suggestion of a patron and friend, Sir Leslie Wilson, who at that time was Governor of Bombay. Sir William admitted the first patients in April, 1931, before his final leave for America. The institution has had an astonishing growth and today it is the largest of its kind in India. It is entirely self-supporting from fees and gifts. In fact the whole plant has been built with Indian donations from a grateful and appreciative public. At first a missionary doctor was in charge, but now for some years one of Dr. Wanless' "boys," an Indian doctor with several degrees, is in charge, and all the staff is Indian. Dr. Wanless' vision and efforts for trained leadership have not been in vain.

The town which has grown up around the sanatorium has recently been named Wanlesstown.

"Sir William Wanless has left as a heritage one of the greatest groups of medical institutions in Asia today, but he has also left us the challenge and inspiration of a noble, devoted, and self-sacrificing life of Christian testimony," said the Rev. Andrew Mutch, D.D., Pastor Emeritus of the Presbyterian Church of Bryn Mawr, Pennsylvania. This church had chosen Dr. Wanless as its foreign mission worker through the Foreign Board, and this close relationship continued throughout the doctor's career.

Three times Dr. Wanless received official honors from Great Britain. He first received the silver Kaiser-I-Hind (Emperor in India) medal of second class in 1912; the same order of gold medal of first class in 1920, in recognition of philanthropic and humanitarian work for India. The third honor was bestowed upon him in 1928 by His Majesty, King George V. This was a Knighthood admitting him to the Order of Knight Bachelor of the British Empire, conferring upon him the degree, honor, and title of Knight Bachelor (K.B.). He was the recipient of a gold Knighthood Medal, and Letters Patent bearing the King's seal. India rejoiced. Receptions were tendered and souvenir gifts heaped upon the modest doctor. Numberless missives of congratulations arrived by wire, cable, and post, notable among them, from his friends, the Viceroy, Lord Irwin; Sir Leslie Wilson, Governor of Bombay; Lord Willingdon, Governor of Madras; and from numerous Rajahs and Indian officials. Sir William's name appeared in the world's " Who's Who," published in London, 1928–1933.

Dr. William James Wanless was united in marriage with Miss Mary Marshall, R.N., of Toronto, Canada, in 1889.

Together they went to India the same year, and for fifteen years Mrs. Wanless helped her husband develop the medical work until her sudden and untimely death of Asiatic cholera. She left a little daughter, Ethel May.

In 1907, Dr. Wanless was united in marriage with Mrs. Lillian Emery Havens, Presbyterian missionary of Kolhapur, India. Until Sir William retired, Lady Wanless gave valuable help in the medical center.

In 1931, after forty-one years of service for India,

Sir William, with his family, made his home at Glendale, California. His death occurred there March 3, 1933. That great soul was called to higher service and all that was mortal was laid to rest in the beautiful mausoleum of Forest Lawn Memorial Park in Glendale. Those left were: the widow, Lady Lillian, and four children, (Mrs. F. W.) Ethel May Trevithick, Harold L., Robert Emery and Margaret Elizabeth.

As has been said, " While those skilful hands are at rest, his soul goes marching on."

" The name of William Wanless will go down in the annals of history as one of the greatest missionaries of his generation," said the well-known Dr. Robert E. Speer, and in speaking of the large group of institutions William Wanless founded, he added, " This great medical center stands as a permanent memorial to a pre-eminently useful servant of God. THIS IS HIS MONUMENT."

CHARLES R. ERDMAN

Former President of the Board of Foreign Missions of the Presbyterian Church in the U.S.A. and Professor of Practical Theology, Emeritus, of Princeton Theological Seminary, Princeton, N. J.

❦ 1 ❧

IT WAS ON A HOT cloudless day that the small S.S. *Mirsapore* chugged into the harbor of Bombay carrying twenty-four year old William Wanless and his bride, Mary. The fiery Indian sun drew out glowing lights in William's sharp brown eyes, while his capable hands grasped an umbrella and a medicine bag. Canadian-born William Wanless was approaching the land of his calling. The occasion was momentous.

Mary searched in her calfskin bag for the letter from Victoria May Hastings. It was not easy to find. She shuffled through a half dozen letters of introduction, boat ticket stubs, identification papers, a pocket Bible, three pressed pansies, a shipboard menu with the notation under fish curry, " This made William seasick," then finally located the letter with the strange Sangli postmark. Quickly unfolding it she read in an excited voice.

" Cora Stiger will meet you at the boat. You can't fail to identify her. She is tall, thin, angular and possessed of a most apparent melancholy."

A line appeared between Mary's large grey eyes.

" William," she asked, " why do you suppose this Cora Stiger is melancholy? "

" Perhaps because she's tall and angular," William answered with a quick glance of approval at Mary's small, well-rounded figure.

" Are you certain she'll meet us? " queried Mary who permitted herself the luxury of worrying over nonessentials.

" If you can't take the word of a missionary," he said, " things have come to a pretty pass." And giving her a smile of confidence he turned his attention to the approaching scene.

Bombay pleased William very much. It was substantial. The foundation looked solid. Starting from the water's edge the city grew up and back, the sturdy Government buildings, the large homes and prosperous stores forming a rising mass which swept up into a firm nest of green hills. Looming up back of the hills started the giant stairway of the gods, the towering Western Ghats. Up, up they soared, each lofty peak stretched higher than the last, until in vaporous mists they disappeared into the heaven-highest clouds.

William drew his gaze back to the harbor. Riding at anchor were ships whose flags seemed to represent every nation; whose holds were being filled with India's hay, tea, spices, fruits, jute, cotton and copra. Past the ships, jutting abruptly from the flat land and dotted with formal gardens and magnificent homes, appeared Malabar Hill. The crests of top-heavy palms traced a winding course taken by well-built roads, while Bombay itself faced the daylight with a sparkling, alabaster face. William's heart throbbed with pride at the evidence of his Empire's achievements in India. And as his heart went out to Bombay, the city seemed to open her heart to him—and he felt warm all over.

But he knew that this was only the gateway to India. This was just the front door. Behind Bombay lay the native India, a land pulsating with humanity—a mysterious humanity ridden by famine, disease, superstition and ignorance. Those people needed him, three hundred million pairs of arms seemed to stretch out imploringly, voices seemed to swell: " Heal us! . . . Heal us! " A mighty impulse to throw his hands outward in a gesture of love and friendship shook the young doctor, but only for a moment. After all, there was his umbrella and his medicine bag.

The ship was coming to anchor now. They were not far from shore.

Beneath her pink, veil-secured bonnet, Mary's grey eyes darted eagerly about the scene before them. Quaint native craft bobbed at the quay; an emerald harbor teemed with sailing vessels and merchant ships; movement of the people on shore formed an ever-changing pattern of color, and she could even make out a crude, cumbersome cart drawn by a hump-shouldered bullock.

" Look, William, look! " exclaimed Mary as she threw discretion and early training to the winds and pointed.

" Yes." His voice was reverent.

"But the colors," insisted Mary, fearful that William was overlooking the physical beauty of the city for its deeper significance.

And William became aware of the colors, the wanton recklessness of the Indian colors. It was as if Nature's paint box had been poured over the mighty Himalayas, releasing pigments which tumbled down over hills and villages and people, leaving a whole country done in richest oils; bodies painted by the sun in every shade of brown; warm, melting gold on arms, in the hair, on the fingers, toes, and in the ears; yellow, red, orange, pink, the saris of the women; men sheathed in white, their turbans green, cerise or rose; a sun-spangled sea of purest blue; the vivid green of palms and the deep purple of far-distant Ghats. No delicate blending here, but primitive colors, unashamed.

"By George!" said William, and out of fairness gave the thrilling colors their due. "They've actually made my heart beat faster." Then he gave himself over to the furious task of disembarking.

Tiny native boats had hurried from shore and now dozens of boatmen screamed their fares, impatient to start back, their bobbing crafts filled with passengers. As if by magic, merchants swarmed the decks, opened bundles containing curios, beads and brassware, and in shrill voices pressed their merchandise upon the visitors. Hot, panting little boats brought apologetic policemen who proceeded with furious argument to push these same merchants off the ship. A naked boy appeared from nowhere and dove on and off the boat, into the water, in dolphin-like pursuit of coins thrown by the curious. Money-changers, custom officials, officers and miscellaneous agents all loudly intent upon their business shouted over the hubbub to the bewildered passengers.

An intense little girl with long black curls and a cold tugged at Mary's hand. "Good-bye, Mrs. Wanless. It's been very pleasant knowing you." And sniffing loudly she hurried after her nurse.

William was shaking hands with a Mr. Whittaker, manager of an indigo plantation. "We'll miss seeing you, Wanless. Drop me a line from your station. Cheerio, young fellow!" And with a courteous bow to Mary he was gone. William's lips tightened. Young fellow! He drew his face into severe lines, hoping to add a few years to his ridiculously youthful appearance.

Other passengers, to whom they had previously said good-bye, were now bobbing about on the small boats, headed for shore. A quick fear stabbed at Mary's heart. Where was Cora Stiger? Why hadn't she come out on one of these small boats to meet them? Was she on shore? Mary strained her eyes in vain for an angular, melancholy figure in the colorful distance, but all looked alike from the boat.

A stateroom door opened down the corridor and a figure emerged. Mary gasped in astonishment as Rao Bahadur Pranspe came upon the deck. She remembered her first glimpse of the distinguished Hindu

when he had boarded the ship at Liverpool. " He's
of the Brahmin caste," William had explained.
" The highest caste of India." But Mary found it
difficult to think of the olive-complexioned man with
the English-tailored suit as a native of India, especially after William had reported several interesting conversations during which Rao Bahadur
Pranspe had spoken flawless English.

Now as the boat anchored in Bombay Harbor, this
Brahmin appeared from his stateroom attired in
native garb. A dhoti of finest white muslin was
topped by a knee-length yellow shirt and green satin
vest. A great turban of soft yellow silk was piled
high on his head, while leather sandals covered otherwise bare feet.

" Look! " Mary's shocked whisper reached her
husband's ears. " Look at Rao Bahadur Pranspe! "

William turned. His eyes lit up and a smile ap-
peared on his face. He was not looking at the
Hindu's costume, but into his eyes. " By George, Mr.
Pranspe," William addressed the dignified Brahmin,
" I'm glad of a chance to shake hands before we go.
We missed you at breakfast this morning." He held
out his hand in a friendly gesture of good will. But
there it stayed, alone and in mid-air.

The olive face of Rao Bahadur Pranspe settled into
caste ridges of arrogance and intolerance. Pausing
only long enough to fix the young people with cobra-
cold eyes, he gave a stiff bow and withdrew from the

defiling presence of the unwelcome foreign Christians.

William felt as if he had been struck a blow. This man had been a friend aboard ship. But now—coming into India . . .

Mary stared indignantly after the receding figure. "That's a nice way for him to act! Did you have a disagreement of some kind? Why is he angry with you?" Her ash-blonde hair quivered under the pink bonnet.

William gave no answer. India didn't seem to be beckoning as fondly now. He took a deep breath.

"I beg your pardon." An excitable, courteous little Englishman approached William, but William didn't hear.

"I say," he repeated and his yellow eyebrows shot up in the middle of his forehead.

William turned. "Yes?"

"Sorry to trouble you, but could you point out a Dr. Wanless to me? I understand he and his wife are on the boat. I'm from the Apollo Hotel," he explained.

"You've come to the right person," William smiled. "I am Dr. Wanless."

The little man drew back shocked. "You?"

William took a deep breath. "Yes. *I* am Dr. Wanless."

"I say!" He struggled to regain his poise. "I rather fancied Dr. Wanless would be an older chap. No offense, young man," he beamed. "I

represent the Apollo Hotel, as I have mentioned.
Fine hotel. Fine appointments. Enjoyed by the
most discriminating Europeans. Fine meals, too, if
I may add, sir." His eyebrows gyrated about, expressing the most incredulous number of emotions,
then they shot upward. " Take your luggage, sir? "

" Yes," said William, wrapping himself in a
mantle of aloof dignity as he gave the man his luggage
checks. How could he make progress in this country
if everyone thought of him as " young fellow "? He
spoke in a deep voice. " We'll stay just one night,
however. We leave for Sangli tomorrow."

" Sangli." The eyebrows quivered. " Oh, yes,
sir! " And off he ran becoming one with the fast
diminishing crowd of agents, passengers, officials and
coolies.

" William! " Mary was scandalized. " How do
you know who he is? Suppose he absconds with our
luggage? "

" I have faith in my fellow man," answered
William, then smiled broadly. " Besides, on his coat
he wore a button which said Apollo Hotel."

When it looked as if they would be the last to leave
the boat, William made a suggestion. " Well, since
Cora Stiger hasn't come to meet us, suppose we go on
shore. She may be waiting there."

Mary, still somewhat ruffled by Rao Bahadur
Pranspe's behavior, consented, and amid a great deal
of vocal direction the two young people boarded a

small native craft and bobbed over the bright water to shore.

"Baksheesh! Baksheesh!" shouted naked children and filthy beggars running through the crowds at the landing. "Jhatka, ride in jhatka," shouted jhatka-wallas indicating their two-wheeled, horse-drawn vehicles. Others yelled, "Ghari! Ghari! Hotel-ghari!" In her excitement Mary forgot her annoyance with the haughty Brahmin and followed closely at William's side as he scanned the milling, gay-colored crowd to catch sight of a woman described as tall, angular and melancholy.

The streets of Bombay teemed with people and animals. Burdened donkeys, weighted camels, horses, bullocks wearing blue beads around their necks wandered through a fabulous setting teeming with Parsee women in finest embroidered saris, Moslem women swathed in white burkas with peep holes of lace for the eyes to see through; Arabs, Afghans, giant Sikhs in their crimson uniforms, pearl-selling Persians, native clerks wearing goggles, fashionably-dressed Europeans and crowds of brown men with white garments and colored turbans. But there was no one answering the description of Cora Stiger.

"Do you think she's forgotten about us?" Mary pulled this fearful thought from the depths of her worry chambers.

"Of course not," soothed William. "She's probably busy." And grasping his medical bag and um-

brella tightly in his left hand, he looked about for a
vehicle to hail. A camel rolled by with leisurely gait,
a crude buffalo-drawn wagon labored past. William
paused, uneasy about this problem of transportation.
A two-seated conveyance pulled by an ancient horse
came down the street. To William's relief the high-
perched driver stopped. " Ghari, sahib? " He indicated that the conveyance was for hire. Nodding a
quick " yes," William helped Mary into the slender
carriage. " Apollo Hotel," he directed and settled
back in the ghari. As they lurched out over the
cobble-stoned streets the two youthful Canadians suddenly found themselves part of the exotic, unbelievable city of Bombay.

The Apollo Hotel helped restore their equilibrium.
" This is something like home," remarked Mary,
heartened by white faces, conventional clothing and
the English tongue. " Now if I only knew where this
Cora Stiger was I'd be happy."

" Well," a spirit of adventure fixed itself upon
William, " let's go look for her."

" You mean—without a guide? "

He laughed. " Mary, India is our home from now
on. We'll have to get acquainted with it. Now, come
along. It's a good day for a drive and you will want
to see the sights before we leave Bombay, anyway."

Mary winced at the thought of the afternoon heat,
but if William wanted to go out, she'd go with him.
She rolled her eyes in despair at the thought of lan-

guage difficulties they might encounter but she was married to a man who always found a solution to every problem, so tucking her arm through his she went gaily, if not tremulously, down the street.

This time William did not pause when confronted with the transportation problem. As a ghari lurched down the street he held up his hand, hailed the driver, and climbed in as if he had lived in India for years. " Miss Stiger's dispensary," he ordered in his most distinct Canadian-English.

The ghari-walla's dark forehead turned into a series of perplexed ridges.

" Medicine place . . . lady medicine place," ventured Mary, speaking loudly in a futile attempt to penetrate with volume the uncomprehending ears.

" Bazaar, sahib? " Eager brown eyes longed for an affirmative nod.

" No," said William firmly and gave silent thanks that they were to be permitted a year in which to learn a most strange-sounding language.

A slight figure in black broadcloth approached, salaamed gracefully and spoke in flawless English.

" May I be of assistance? " he asked.

William beamed. " Thank you very much, friend. Would you kindly ask this driver to take us to Cora Stiger's dispensary? "

There was a moment's hesitation. Their new friend lowered his dark eyes tactfully. His stiff, shiny black hat sparkled in the sun. " Perhaps it would be best if you did not go there."

"But we must. You see, Miss Stiger's expecting us."

The shoulders shrugged in a fatalistic Indian gesture. "Perhaps it is best this way." And turning to the furrow-browed driver he gave curt directions.

"I appreciate your help," said William warmly, starting to offer his hand.

"William!" Mary cut in sharply, recalling vividly the rebuffed handshake on the boat.

But much to her surprise the man shook William's hand with a graceful gesture, then bowing graciously stood to one side as the ghari clattered off.

William tapped the ghari-walla on the shoulder. "Parsee?" he queried.

The driver looked over his shoulder as William indicated the friendly man they had left behind. His full lips parted in a joyous grin. "Parsee, sahib," he nodded vigorously. "Parsee."

William sank back beside Mary. "Parsee," he assured her, while she stared in amazement.

"William Wanless, what in the world are you talking about?"

"The man I just shook hands with. He was a Parsee." Adjusting his white topee bought in Port Said as protection from the tropical sun, he launched into a learned bit of information. "Parsees are adherents of the religion of Zoroaster, having fled from Persia in the seventh and eighth centuries. The majority settled in Bombay, and although comparatively few in number, have tremendous influence for enlightenment. They educate their children, do not observe purdah, make a lot of money and are most cooperative with the Government.'' He crossed his knees and beamed upon his open-mouthed wife.

Mary stared at him a moment, then her eyes narrowed. '' How do you know ? '' she demanded, a curl falling down over one eye.

William cleared his throat, raised his eyebrows and stared at her over his nose. '' My dear,'' he informed her, '' I read it in a book.''

Mary pretended to be busy with the errant curl, but she was so pleased with her husband that her eyes almost laughed out loud.

The ghari had gone through the European section and now turned into a street which was breath-taking. They had left one world, the world of white men and their influence, and had come into another. No longer were the shops well-kept, glass-paned and neat. These were open stalls, facing on the dusty street. Their ghari-walla was screaming at the crowds in the street to '' make way for the sahib and mem-sahib! '' Mary clutched at William's sleeve and plunged her nose into a handkerchief as a meat market was passed. Great, red chunks of meat lay about on pieces of wood. Entrails, heads and leavings decorated the earthen floor while the squatting shopkeeper, his friends, implements and merchandise bristled with huge, black, hungry flies.

The crowds were dense. Dirty men with white or red streaks on their foreheads, dusky women, only a

few without the red forehead dot marking them as
wives, illy-kept children and cattle roamed at will.
Tiny shops gaped with purple grapes and bright
oranges, exquisitely hand-woven cloth and shining
hammered brass. But over everything and everyone
swarmed the persistent flies. William marveled that
any were free from disease.

He also marveled at the thought of a woman, alone,
ministering help in the midst of this squalor and
filth.

Opinions about Cora Stiger varied. William could
still hear the frog-like voice of old Dr. Thomas as
he pronounced a most unfavorable judgment upon
her. As a group of students disbanded after a delicate eye operation at the University of New York's
medical department, Cora's name had come up.
William recalled how Dr. Thomas had methodically pulled off his rubber gloves while saying,
" She's a misfit. A woman who has so many conflicts
in her own mind that she has to go out and settle the
disputes of the world." He'd slapped his gloves into
the sink and abruptly dismissed the unpleasant subject. But there were other opinions. Before leaving
Toronto William had occasion to speak with a middle-
aged spinster whose travels had included India and a
visit to Cora's dispensary and the spinster had loyally
declared Miss Stiger to be " nothing less than a
saint." Then there was Victoria May Hastings'
report: " Tall, angular, thin, melancholy."

Well, he'd make up his mind for himself. Best not
to be guided by others' opinions.

Their carriage came to a halt. William thought
there must be a mistake. There was no dispensary
here. Just open stalls along the curb. The obliging
driver turned around. "Dispensary," he said with
no little difficulty and William followed his pointing
finger and found himself looking into the stall of a
native Hindu medicine man.

"Bother!" said William. "He's gotten his directions mixed."

"Dispensary, sahib," insisted the ghari-walla.

A swarm of curious passers-by gathered quickly
about the ghari.

"We'll soon settle this," William assured his wife,
and jumping down from the carriage approached the
medicine man who was in the midst of a spirited
diagnosis. The patient, a short, voluble man, doubled
up in distress as the learned one poked an inquiring
finger at his stomach. The wails of the patient were
shrill and bystanders chatted and tossed in bits of information as the medicine man redoubled his efforts.
Then came a hurried, whispered conference with the
weeping wife and to William's surprise the medicine
man took up a pen and scribbled words of Hindu on a
slip of paper.

"A prescription," approved William, but at that
moment the patient grabbed the paper, stuffed it into
his mouth and swallowed hard. The medicine man

clasped his hands, salaamed, and the patient and wife departed, satisfied with "the cure."

William paused a moment to regain his perspective, then approached the man whose elaborate coiffure bore testimony to the effectiveness of cow dung mixed with sandalwood oil.

"I'm looking for Miss Stiger—Cora Stiger," began William, hoping this strange, wild-eyed man might understand English.

The medicine man broke into a mercenary grin. "Sahib sick?" he queried. "Medicine?" His gesture included what passed for medicines laid out on a filthy square of dirty white cotton on the ground. As William gazed upon the revolting display of dried snakes, ground up powders, strange-colored pills and slips of papers, he thought of the spotless, scientific hospitals of his training and it was with difficulty that he controlled a desire to snatch up the soiled cloth and scatter these ridiculous remedies to the winds. But he had come to India not to tear down the old, but to build up the new.

"I'm looking for Cora Stiger," William repeated.

The grin again. Then the medicine man spoke. "Not here," he said with evident delight.

"Can you tell me where she is?" William disliked the man's obvious insolence.

Again came the fateful shrug of the shoulders. "No, sahib. Gone." And he turned away.

"But, I say," insisted William, "you must know where!"

" Gone, sahib," came the irritating answer.

" How long has she been gone? " After all, the woman couldn't have disappeared off the face of Bombay.

" Not know, sahib," shrugged the Hindu. " Not know."

It was obvious the man did know but was just being exasperating. William drew some money from his pocket. The medicine man's eyes became as sharp as the eyes of a trained falcon. " How long has she been gone? " William asked again as the dirty hand closed over the money.

" One week, sahib," nodded the man.

" Good. Now, where did she go? " William asked. The eyes were sharper still. " Don't know, sahib," but the tone was plainly asking for more money.

William's temper flared with a sudden thought. " He's taking advantage of me because I look so infernally young! " He drew himself up straight and strode back to the ghari as beggars and little boys swarmed about him with outstretched palms.

" Baksheesh! . . . Baksheesh! " they cried in the perpetual wail of India.

" Apollo Hotel," William shouted to the driver, and the sway-backed horse worked its way through crowds in the native bazaar toward the European settlement.

Mary, having never seen her husband angry with anyone before, became exceedingly curious. " What did he say? " she wanted to know. And then with a flashing eye, " And how dare he say it? "

" It was nothing, Mary," he answered swatting at a fly.

" Why, William Wanless, you were furious and don't tell me you weren't. I could tell by the way you ground your heels into the ground."

William composed himself by winding his gold watch. " I wasn't angry with the man, Mary. But I am angry with the system. Why, he was a doctor— a medicine man, at least." He exploded. " And did you ever see such filth and dirt and stupidity in your life? No wonder the death rate is unbelievable. I'm amazed that any of them are alive. Bah! " This last exclamation as a sacred cow contaminated a fruit stall with no protest from the squatting owner.

Mary shuddered. " You'd think they'd know better," she managed, at a loss for words.

" It isn't the people. It's their ideas. Show them a better way, Mary, and they'll take it." He patted her hand and spoke with great confidence. " That's why we're here. To show them a better way." His renewed confidence found expression in song and Mary was treated to stirring variations of " Go Labor On, Spend and Be Spent," all the way back to the Hotel.

William made no mention of Cora Stiger until later in the evening at dinner.

The elegance of the Apollo dining room, the sumptuous, twelve-course meal, the interesting assortment

of European diners and the even swishing of heat-
disturbing punkahs had captured Mary's excited attention. Now she turned at William's exclamation.

" What an unfortunate idea the natives get about
our race," he frowned disapproval upon the endless
bottles of spirits circulating freely upon the table of
fellow diners.

" Why, dear? " asked Mary, gazing regretfully at
the plate of delectable Indian confections before her
and wishing she hadn't eaten both fish curry and
chicken *pilau.*

William examined the yellow mango on his plate,
then experimentally spooned into it. " To the Indian
every white man is a Christian. Even that fellow,"
and he indicated an unsteady, monocled son of the
Empire who was carrying on an earnest conversation
with a champagne bottle.

William's disapproval of the unsteady one was
brought to an abrupt halt as he sampled his first bite
of Indian mango. " By George! " The indescribable
flavor soothed his whole being. " Mary, taste this,"
he directed and loading the spoon with mango lifted
it to her lips.

" Oh, William, I couldn't," she protested thinking
of the twelve consumed courses, then opened her
mouth. As she tasted the exquisite fruit, Mary experienced one phase of India's constant lure and
rapture.

" Mango madness." Some months later the prim
Victoria May Hastings was to give the words a

vicious sound as she pronounced judgment upon addicted natives. But, to her surprise, William and Mary Wanless had only sympathy for those with "mango madness." The older woman didn't know they had once tasted and always remembered the delights of the strange native fruit at the Hotel Apollo.

The monocled one, courteously escorting two champagne bottles, teetered out of the dining room. William keenly felt the need for constructive action. "We must find Cora Stiger the first thing in the morning," he crisply informed Mary.

It was late that evening when the knock came at their door. Mary was repairing some torn lace on a petticoat while William inspected the construction of their hotel room. It was a good-sized room with painted white walls and great windows permitting much-needed ventilation. Rough Indian matting covered the floor and the ever-present mosquito net surrounded the wooden bed. William was just remarking to Mary that "we'll probably be sleeping under this stuff for the next forty years," when the knock sounded.

"Who do you suppose that is?" Mary addressed the question to William although he made no pretense of being clairvoyant.

"Let's find out." And with characteristic directness he opened the door.

Standing in the hallway was a woman. All his life

William remembered the picture she made that night. At first he couldn't see her face. The hallway was dim, a few kerosene lamps fought to penetrate the Indian darkness, but only caused gloomy shadows to crawl strangely along the corridor. She stood in the doorway, a tall, thin, angular figure—and when she spoke there was melancholy.

" I'm looking for Dr. Wanless." Her lonely voice penetrated the room, and William knew that this was Cora Stiger.

He made his welcome hearty and sincere. " Come in, Miss Stiger! Mary, see who's here. By George, we've been looking for you! " And clasping her hand warmly William guided her into the room.

Mary dropped her sewing and turned with joyous welcome to the newcomer. How she had wanted to meet Cora Stiger, to come face to face with a truly selfless being. But as she approached, Mary faltered. She felt no response. She tried to smile up into the eyes of this tall woman, but the eyes that looked down were strangely cold. The long, thin hand that lay in hers was like ice.

" Won't you sit down? " Mary heard herself saying, and the thin figure seemed to fold up like a deck chair and came to rest on the grass matting.

The lonely voice explained. " Indians sit on the floor." And there was silence.

" Well, this *is* a pleasure." William's good, sensible voice brought back courage to Mary's pinched heart. " We went to the native quarters this afternoon looking for your dispensary but discovered you'd moved.'' Cora gave no reply but sat motionless, her face shadowed by a red native scarf worn over her flat, brown hair.

'' We were disappointed not to find you when we landed, but I suppose you were busy.'' William's statement was in the form of an indirect question. He was trying to draw out this strange, silent woman. Still Cora sat motionless.

Perhaps I'm chattering too much for her, thought William, and turned over the conversation with these words: '' Now, tell us about your work here. Do the natives appreciate your help? ''

Cora lifted her eyes, looked at William, then at Mary who hoped her heart didn't sound as if it was thumping out loud. When the pale, blue eyes were turned back on William, Cora spoke . . . and her tones were like those of a prophet.

'' Go home. They don't want us. Go.'' The thin, purple-veined lids covered pale blue eyes and from her hair slipped the red shawl.

'' Well,'' replied William, '' that's not exactly encouraging advice to give a young medical missionary.''

The pale eyes stared into his. '' Go home,'' Cora repeated, but this time her voice was not the same. Broken threads of hysteria raveled its even edges.

'' Now, see here, Miss Stiger,'' William could be helpfully matter-of-fact, '' I don't understand your giving us such advice.''

The slender woman seemed to observe him for the first time. " Why, you're just a boy," she exclaimed in shocked tones. " I didn't dream you'd be so young. These people have no respect for youth. You're wasting your time here. Please go home."

She had hit William's touchiest point. He thrust out his jaw stubbornly.

" I intend to do nothing of the kind. I was called to India. I shall remain in India."

Cora Stiger was fast losing her calm and composure. The long, icy fingers nervously twisted the red scarf and her thin lips quivered. Her face was pale and her eyes deep-set.

William stared intently. Evidently the woman was not herself. Not wishing to agitate her further he abruptly changed the subject.

" Mrs. Wanless and I had a very pleasant crossing. No bad weather at all. It's Mary's first trip outside of Canada," he confessed with a little laugh. Mary joined the conversation.

" William studied to be a doctor in New York, you know. But I took my nurse's training in Toronto."

The melancholy woman on the floor continued to stare at them without comment. Mary looked helplessly toward William.

" Miss Stiger," William spoke abruptly, " what's the matter with you ? " It was his turn to stare. The thin lips quivered again, tears formed in the weak, blue eyes.

"I'm warning you. Go home! Go home!" And she broke into quick, harsh sobs.

Instantly Mary knelt on the floor beside her. "Don't cry," she pleaded. "Please don't cry. Oh, William, perhaps she's ill."

But Cora Stiger pushed the soft arms away. William motioned Mary aside. "If it's medical help you need," he offered, "I'll do all I can to help you."

Cora Stiger was fighting to control her tears. "India doesn't want you. You don't belong here. They're a different kind of people." Her eyes narrowed. "They're not human," she breathed.

"Come, come," William's voice was as refreshing as a salt breeze, "don't worry about us. We're hardy, Mary and I. Now, let me get you a cup of tea."

But Cora Stiger didn't hear. Her eyes were glazed and she stared at the grass rug hypnotically. "I was going to help these people, too. I was going to do great things in India. I wanted to be one of the people." Her voice trembled. "I thought I was dealing with human beings, but they aren't. These people worship lust. They worship filth, immorality, foulness!" Her agitated voice rose harshly. "And they're so repulsive! They're so damnably repulsive!" Her control was gone. She sobbed again. William was alarmed at this fierce tirade.

"Miss Stiger," William said kindly, "you need to go back home for a while."

She straightened up as if lashed. "What, and

acknowledge my failure?" There was a pause. "I thought I was a fine social worker. I came here filled with ideas. I've talked and I've worked, I've done everything the books tell you to do—and I'm a failure. They don't want what we white people have to give. It's too good for them!" Her unhappy fingers clawed a hole in the red scarf, but she was not aware of it.

"Mary," William directed, "get her a cup of tea."

Mary started toward the door, but the figure on the floor stopped her. "No," she said, and her voice was resigned and sad like the wind sighing through an ancient mogul's tomb. "Tea won't help." She uncoiled herself from the rug and stood upright, taller by a head than even William.

"I only wanted to save you what I've gone through," she whispered. "Of course, you have your surgery, your medicine. The only medicine I had was the common type—pills, powders and physics. They did some good." Her eyes glazed over slightly. "And—you have your religion." Her voice sounded far away. "You know, I once tried to convert someone to Christianity. She was only nine, but I showed her pictures, told her Bible stories, sang hymns for her. But—her family placed her in a temple." Cora's voice grew bitter. "You'll learn what temple girls are!" Tears trembled down the pale face. "I wanted to save this one. I loved her. She was so innocent—and gentle. And those priests——"

Burying her face in her hands, Cora shuddered, and the tragedy of her emotion filled the room.

Mary felt totally unable to cope with the strength of this woman's failure and shrank into a corner of the room, hoping that William would take a hand and *do* something. William did.

"Miss Stiger, do you believe in God?"

The abruptness of the question startled her. She eyed William defensively.

"Of course I do!"

"Doesn't he clearly tell us in His Word that His good will overcome evil?"

"I've read the Bible on and off for ten years, my friend," she said grimly. "But . . ." Here she sighed, and William experienced a shock as she lifted her shoulders in the expressive, defeated gesture he had seen on the streets of Bombay. She drew her scarf tightly about her shoulders. "Before you decide to stay, I advise you to look at one of India's goddesses. Around the corner from my—my old dispensary," her voice nearly broke, "you'll find her temple. Go inside, see her image and remember— that's one of their deities. Her name is . . . Kali." As she uttered the name a weakness overcame her. The young doctor and his wife rushed to her side. She seemed to be fainting. They helped her into a chair and William crossed to the dresser, pouring a glass of water from the brass pitcher.

As Mary stood by her side, Cora reached out with thin fingers and caught her arm. "Go home," she hissed. " Go home! " And pulling her scarf about her whispered " Good-bye," and was gone.

" Miss Stiger! Miss Stiger! " William hurried into the hallway, but the tall figure had disappeared down the stairs. " By George," said William coming into the room and closing the door, " I don't think she's well enough to be out alone."

But Mary didn't hear him. She was lying across the bed saying to herself, " I won't be frightened! I won't be frightened! I won't! "

Later, as the quiet, fresh air stirred in the room and humming mosquitoes tried in vain to penetrate the netting, Mary wondered if she and William should heed Cora's warning, or at least talk about it. She wondered intermittently all night long, for the sound of barking dogs, chattering natives, a weird singer and incessantly throbbing temple drums kept her awake. As the quick Indian dawn broke she decided against it. There was nothing to be afraid of. Besides, William was with her.

At seven o'clock a discreet knock sounded on the door and a smiling, white-robed, pink-turbaned figure entered with chota hazri. Everybody in India enjoys chota hazri, the servant explained, for breakfast is never served until nine o'clock. As Mary curiously looked under the large linen napkin spread over the tray, she discovered to her joy that chota hazri was the delightful combination of tea and toast. William, ordinarily not adventurous as far as foreign food

habits were concerned, immediately adopted the chota
hazri custom remarking that this was an Indian custom of which he heartily approved.

" Our train leaves at two," William announced
briskly, crunching the last crust of toast. " How
would you like to make a few purchases at the bazaar?
The European bazaar," he hastened to add. Mary's
eyes grew bright. She adored shopping. " I'll be
ready in half a second, William," she promised.
Half an hour later she was fully dressed and ready to
go.

" Well, what will please your fancy? " he asked
magnanimously enjoying his wife's eagerness.

" First," said Mary, " I want to buy some furniture. We'll need some at Sangli I'm sure."

" Very well," assented William.

" And," sighed Mary, " I just want to sort of look
around."

William smiled. " To the European bazaar,
driver," he ordered and the ghari started toward the
place said by the Englishman with the gyrating eyebrows to be the delight of every resident and traveler
in Bombay.

Ten minutes later, alighting from the carriage,
Mary's eyes grew round as clay saucers. " William! "
she cried, staring down one whole wing of a building
containing stalls heaped high with foodstuffs, " did
you ever see so much to eat before in all your life?
And there," pointing to another wing heavy with
fragrance, " look at the flowers. Millions of them!

Oh, dear, I don't know which to look at first. And then I want to see the furniture, too. Let's look at the food stalls," and pulling him by the arm she started down an aisle which William laughingly called " the epicure's delight."

" My dear," ventured William as they came upon a stall piled high with exotic fruits, " I may leave you to look around for yourself. I'll be back within an hour."

Mary's eyes were excited by the display of purple grapes, thick yellow plantains and bright oranges from Nagpur, but she turned from them with a frown.

" Oh, no," she was very positive. " I'm not going to be left alone in any strange place like Bombay." And linking her gloved hand possessively through his arm she quoted, " Where you go I'll go," and the little white feather on her pink bonnet bobbed with the decided nod of her head.

" Well, suit yourself. I thought I'd go look up Cora Stiger this morning. See if I can be of some help to the poor woman." William's youthful face was full of the milk of human kindness.

The unmistakable odor of fresh fish assailed their nostrils. Mary glanced at the booth with the thrilling display of oysters, the appetizing palla fish known as the salmon of India, the exotic pomfret, and the inevitable bombie, English Bombay duck which she discovered to her surprise isn't a duck at all but a glutenous fish salted and dried. How she longed to

investigate these oddities. If only the Cora Stiger
episode hadn't happened. It was so morbid and Miss
Stiger was so unhappy.

" Perhaps—well, perhaps she doesn't want to see
us any more," offered Mary, while William turned a
look of reproach upon his lovely bride.

" Where there is a soul in need there is work to be
done," he admonished. His jaw set firmly. " Let's
not permit the gewgaws and folderol of the bazaar to
interfere with important things."

Mary looked regretfully upon a booth filled with
poultry. Fowl, duck, turkey, snipe, curlew and teal
reposed in alluring display.

" You may stay if you care to," William spoke
helpfully. " In fact, I wish you would. I think
you'd enjoy shopping here."

Mary cast a regretful look at the unexplored aisles
of booths. " No, I'll go with you," she announced
and they pushed their way through the crowds of
Hindus, Mahrattas, Gujarati people and Europeans
and once more found themselves in a ghari, only this
time it had an old driver and a young horse.

" Where does Cora Stiger live? " asked Mary, casting apprehensive glances at the direction in which
they were moving, for she recognized the approach to
the squalid native section.

" I gave directions to the driver," William answered. " The fellow at the desk looked it up for me
this morning."

There were fewer Europeans on the streets

now . . . and more, many more tattered brown people.

Mary peered through the dust. " Oh, William," she felt squeamish. " What is that man doing? "

As they approached the object of her exclamation both experienced a revulsion of feeling. From his reading on India William recognized this individual as a holy man. One arm was held high over his head, a long skinny arm which looked mummified, while corkscrew fingernails hung like long claws. The man had evidently held his arm in such a position for years. Mary stared at the fierce, dried-up, wild face smeared with white ashes and oil, at the matted hair straggling about his scrawny neck and emaciated shoulders. William explained why he was a holy man. He had done penance and conquered his body.

" Ughhh," shuddered Mary pressing close to her husband.

But William took another attitude. " My dear," his voice was grave, " we must be very careful as to our attitude regarding these people. If we look only at the outer forms we may be revolted. Yes, I'm *certain* we'll be revolted," he added catching a glimpse of a beggar whose face was covered with running sores. " We must always look into their eyes. And we must see there the love of God. Just look deep into their eyes, Mary, and remember what I told you. We must see Love." And summoning up his spiritual strength to put his theory into practice, William gazed with loving calm at the hordes of dirty, diseased native people, seeing in each man his brother.

Ancient, once-white houses with overhanging balconies lined the streets. Goats, dogs, cows and swarms of naked children crowded together. Reeking with odors of rancid grease, curry powder, oil of cocoanut and withered jasmine flowers, putrid with filth and pestilence, this was the residential section of the poorer Hindus.

Mary tried to imagine how Cora could possibly live here. The reason for her despondency became clearer. White people *couldn't* live like this, she thought, and William said, " *Nobody* should live in filth like this."

The horse stopped. An excited crowd blocked a doorway and interrupted traffic through the street. Babbling women carried on their hips naked, bangled babies, little girls screamed in shrill voices, bands of small boys darted about while an official tried to command order.

" Stand back, stand back! " the policeman called, as an agile brown boy darted toward the doorway.

William tapped the ghari-walla on the shoulder. " What's going on? " he queried, accompanying his question with gestures.

The driver, who understood English, shrugged his shoulders. " Not know, sahib. This is house." And he pointed to the house with the crowd.

" Oh, dear," trembled Mary. " Something's happened to her. Wait. I'll go in, too."

"No." William spoke with a strong note of finality. "You stay right where you are." And he stepped from the ghari and made his way through the babbling crowd to the busy policeman.

"I beg your pardon." The sound of English brought a look of joy to the perspiring face of the moustached policeman. The fellow attempted a brisk salute, but a small boy clung to his coat sleeve, making it impossible.

"I'm looking for Cora Stiger," William began.

They were at the doorway now. "You go on in," directed the officer. "The doctor will talk with you. Blakely!" he called. "A friend of the deceased."

William caught his breath. The deceased.

Blakely, a stubby man wearing a wrinkled white suit, turned at the sound of his name. "Oh," he wheezed, "how do, son," and held out his damp hand to William.

William smarted hotly at this allusion to his youthful appearance, but shook the damp hand with conventional courtesy. His eyes traveled to a corner of the sparsely furnished room. There, lying on a low cot, was Cora Stiger. William had the strange feeling that she looked warmer in death than she had in life.

The puffy little doctor was explaining. "Just got here a minute ago. It was sleeping tablets. Never could get to sleep at night was her trouble. Got an overdose, I guess." He blew his nose. "Any special directions? You're a friend of hers, I take it."

" Yes," said William softly, and drawing out of his pocket the money Mary was to have used at the bazaar, thrust it upon the doctor. " See that she is given a decent burial, will you? "

" Right. Glad to oblige," answered the puffy little man, and William walked out of the cheerless room, glad to get away from the squalid place.

Mary could tell the news was grave as she looked at his face. She pressed his hand.

" Dead," murmured William. " Overdose of sleeping tablets."

A cold chill shot through Mary. " Not—on purpose? " she managed.

William stared at her. He hadn't considered that before. " I don't know," he said slowly, then shook his head. " No, of course not! " Then he warned, " And don't you start worrying," but his voice lacked its usual confidence. Suddenly he sat bolt upright. " Driver," he commanded. " Back that way! That way! " He pointed toward the squalid native section. The ghari-walla nodded and turned his horse.

Mary protested. " Not again today. Please, William."

He clasped her hands tightly. " There's something we must see." And putting his arm about her held her close as they went through the native section.

Presently William looked up—ordered the ghari to stop. Before them was a Hindu temple. Massive with ornate carvings, heavy with the dust of centuries, the temple seemed to rise with rugged mag-

nificence from out of the ground. The courtyard
teemed with worshippers milling about the center of
the open space and forming an unending procession
back and forth from the holy of holies, the inner
temple where the goddess was enthroned. As the
worshippers shifted about, Mary gasped, grabbed
William's arm and pointed. Like a fresh red wound
in the center of the courtyard a flat altar reared up,
slimy with blood. At its side a decapitated sheep lay
in a heap while with religious fervor devotees
groveled on the ground, smeared themselves with the
red gore, splashed it over their faces, arms and necks.

Mary felt sick at her stomach. William put his
arm about her, gently guided her through the courtyard with him.

" What is this place? " she protested squeamishly.

" The Shrine of Kali," he answered low. " The
goddess that Cora Stiger mentioned." Then as an
afterthought. " She's the goddess of blood sacrifice."
Mary writhed at the thought of the sheep, wondered
how long since the victims had not been animal, but
human.

Pushing their way unobtrusively through the
crowd, William moved slowly toward the temple as its
mighty doors swung open, permitting more worshippers to enter, others to leave, then closed. " We'll go
closer," he whispered and together they worked their
way near the temple doors.

Drums beat incessantly; the wailing chants of the
priests mingled weirdly with jangling bells as the exe-

cutioner raised his great sword and with a shriek another sheep was beheaded. The stench of blood under the hot sun was nauseating. The worshippers clogged the opening of the temple as their bodies caught and held the great doors, and then William and Mary caught a glimpse of the fierce blood goddess, Kali.

Gleaming in the dim light of lamps, smeared with butter and oil, the monstrous idol glared with goggling eyes through masses of black, coarse hair. Pagan and fierce in her stance, she ground the figure of a man beneath her feet. From a purple-hued body emerged a massive head, a vicious mouth with lolling red tongue dripping blood. From her shoulders writhed four sinuous arms. One hand held the decapitated head of a man, another the gory beheading knife, a third pointed toward heaven and a fourth pointed down toward hell.

William gazed, fascinated. So this was Kali. Kali, the Goddess of Blood Sacrifice. Mary whimpered; with a frightened cry she turned and would have run away, but William grasped her firmly.

" Look at her, Mary," he commanded, and though his voice was low it rang with determination. " Look at her and through her and never, never be afraid."

Mary did as she was told, but her heart beat with a new terror. William stared long at the four frightening hands—tense and terrible in their demands, and suddenly he felt the stir of a mighty challenge. He flexed his fingers until the knuckles grew white. He was face to face with an idol which caught up and symbolized in her fierce body India's challenge to him—a challenge that was savage, ominous, and ancient as the secrets of a tomb.   And pitted against its dark defiance—were his own two hands.

As WILLIAM STARED at his hands, they seemed to take on a new meaning. He became aware of the scar on his wrist, a white, ragged scar carried from the age of ten. William always remembered the excitement he had caused on that cold day back in Toronto. He was only ten, but possessed of tremendous vigor and an exhilaration caused by nippy weather, had set about to cut down a small tree in the nearby forest. But the axe was heavy, and the young woodsman inexperienced—a combination which spelled disaster.

Ten minutes later the family, listening spellbound as Father read a bloodcurdling news account about General Custer's last stand in Montana, was abruptly treated to the shocking sight of a member of their own family dripping blood and wailing at the top of his lungs.

Unlike General Custer, William was not beyond repair. Mother's capable hands washed and bound the wound and with painstaking nursing brought him through intact. Mother had often said, " Had the axe cut half an inch deeper, young man . . ." and then she always shuddered and stopped.

" Say, William," the sharp voice of his good friend, Bert Briggs, cut across his memory, " I dare you to play lacrosse with us! "

This challenge had come when the family first moved to Toronto, the year the whole of Canada had been shaken by the fire which swept over six hundred acres near the city of St. John in New Brunswick. William had hesitated. Up to that time he'd never been attracted to sports. A rapidly-growing family threw more and more chores upon the shoulders of the older children and William took his share. But lacrosse looked fascinating. He longed to grasp one of the hooked sticks and try to land the little ball into its cup. So he accepted Bert's challenge. Bert was always sorry he had offered the challenge, for William not only became captain of the team, but won the prize cup three years in a row.

A sense of power in his hands had always thrilled the Canadian boy. Whether it was handling a lacrosse stick, counting out change from behind a counter in his father's hardware store, or shoveling snow from the doorway of their unpretentious home, his hands had always felt strong with power—that is until a certain spring day in 1883.

It was seven o'clock in the morning when William awoke and felt the pain. He was annoyed. The sunlight streaming through the uncurtained window of his small attic bedroom stabbed viciously at his eyelids. An oppressive heaviness seemed to have fallen onto his broad chest during the night. It was hard to breathe.

" This is ridiculous," announced the eighteen-year-old young man and sat bolt upright.

Instantly the small attic room spun in furious circles. The rocker, desk and bureau seemed to whiz about with William sitting in their midst. He fell back on his hard pillow and gritted his teeth. William Wanless was not used to being sick. In the first place he was too busy enjoying life to take the time, and in the second place he insisted, with Scotch stubbornness, that sickness was not for men.

He opened his sharp brown eyes to see if the furniture had stopped whirling. It had. The ancient, marble-topped bureau brought from Jedborough, Scotland, by his pioneer grandfather, stood stolidly beside the brick chimney. His flat, pine-board desk, squeezed into a corner of the tiny room, attested to the handiwork of William's eldest brother, Thomas. Thomas had been the family " fixer," and when he married and left home two years before, nearly every piece of furniture in the big, old-fashioned, two-story house bore testimony to Thomas' " fixability."

On this desk rested William's private library: " Pilgrim's Progress," a King James Bible, and " Travels of Livingstone." Here he also labored painstakingly over his small accounts, after-school salary earned working in Father's hardware store, the disposition of such earnings, money lent—but never borrowed, and a tiny, but persistently growing lump sum.

As William turned his eyes from the comforting darkness of the shadowed corners and glared challengingly into the sunlight, the pain stabbed again.

" William! "

It was Mother's voice from downstairs calling him
to breakfast. Elizabeth Wanless had a good, substantial voice. She was able to convey in one word exactly
what she meant. Father could, too. John Wanless'
voice was as rough as a Scotch burr and just as positive. When he lifted it in song each Sunday at the
Dunn Street Presbyterian Church, those near him
had to sing for sheer relief, for John Wanless could
shake the rafters when he liked a hymn.

From below William could hear his little brother,
Archibald, screeching at sister Elizabeth because
she'd snatched his red rubber ball, and then Father's
words commanding Monday-morning discipline.

The heartening odor of home-made sausage drifted
temptingly into the attic bedroom and caused William
to be completely out of sympathy with his condition.
William liked sausage. He also liked the morning
meal, the warmth of the pungent kitchen, the activity
of his brothers and sisters, Mother's ample, aproned
figure bustling about the big wood stove, and the
sincere moment of grace, as a quiet fell over the noisy
children and Father said " Thank you " to God.

A brisk knock sounded on the bedroom door. That
would be Annie. William tried to answer but the
words stuck in his throat.

The knock was repeated.

" Annie," William managed to gasp, and hoped his
favorite sister would come in and somehow rescue him
from this foolish and annoying dilemma.

Annie peeked in curiously. She was not beautiful, an unfortunate circumstance in those days for a girl of twenty who was still unmarried, but she had a merry mirthfulness and played a substantial organ accompaniment to William's cornet solos.

Through the partially open door she called, " Oh, oh! What will Father say when he finds out you haven't swept the store this morning? "

There was no answer. Annie laughed. " Are you playing 'possum? " she said and striding into the room snatched a glass of water off the bureau and ran toward the bed, prepared to use " The Grandpa Wanless Method " of arousing late sleepers. Suddenly she stopped.

" William! " There was anxiety in her high voice. How strange William looked. Noticing his flushed face, she came to his bedside and with long, tapering fingers felt his forehead.

Mother's voice hurried up the stairs and into the bedroom. " Come to breakfast." The finality in Mother's tone indicated that this was positively the last call. William heard the scrambling of feet, the eager scraping of chairs, as the family gathered around the round oak table, anticipation in their eyes and appetites. There was no question in the youth's mind—he wanted to join them. Enough of this sickness! William sat up, and fell right back again.

Annie's alarm grew. In spite of her sturdy pioneer ancestors, sister Annie was absolutely helpless in the face of sickness. " I—I think I'd better call

Mother," she faltered, and before William could protest she had fled from the room.

For no logical reason William grew angry. Why
couldn't Annie stay and do something for him? Why
did she have to run for help the minute a fellow felt
bad? William gasped for breath. Something was
wrong with his chest.

Well, he'd have to be better by Wednesday. This
was Monday. Of course, by Wednesday he'd be feeling fine and ready for his lacrosse game. But suppose he wasn't better?

William started to worry. He'd have to be at that
game. He had promised the team. It was his duty.
And the word " duty " to William James Wanless
was a sacred word.

The dutiful young man closed his eyes. Not
because he couldn't hold them open, he told himself
stubbornly, but because of the unnatural brightness
of the sun.

He must have fallen asleep, for when William
again opened his eyes Dr. Huntley was standing by
the small, iron bed.

" A sick boy. A very sick boy," murmured the
doctor, nervously polishing his bald spot with a dingy
handkerchief.

" What appears to be the trouble, Doctor? "
Father's big voice boomed from the squeaky, ma-
hogany rocker.

A moment elapsed while the greyed handkerchief

again traveled over the bald head. " I'm not certain, but it looks like pneumonia."

A muffled sob sounded and Annie, who had come back fortified by the presence of her mother, father, and Dr. Huntley, fled from the room. The squeak of the rocker ceased. It was Mother's voice, sharp and taut, that caused William's wandering mind to focus.

" If it's pneumonia we must know—immediately! "

Father became wonderfully gentle. " Now, Mother, patience, patience."

Mother's face was stiff, and when she spoke it seemed difficult for her to move her lips. " How can we be sure? "

The handkerchief was fluttering uncertainly about the doctor's hesitant person, and William had a feeling that his mother wanted to snatch it and use it to whip Dr. Huntley into aggressive action. The doctor fumed and puttered about in the depths of an aged black medical bag. Father patted Mother's shoulder tenderly and just before William closed his eyes he glanced down at his hands. They looked so ridiculously helpless lying there on the quilt.

The following five days seemed to be without end. William's head throbbed continuously, the weight on his chest seemed unbearable, and breathing became an almost impossible task. Long, coma-like periods merged into waking intervals filled with tear-stained, familiar faces, anxious whispers, the voice of Dr. Huntley and the heartbreaking realization that Wednesday had come and gone and no one would give him the game score. "My team must have lost," William moaned, tossing restlessly.

His fierce, labored breathing echoed through the quiet house and cast an ominous pall over every heart except that of five-year-old Archibald who callously announced that he hoped his brother would die because he liked funerals.

Mother's impatience and fear reached a breaking point Saturday morning. "We're calling in another doctor," she announced. Dr. Huntley nervously agreed that he would welcome a consultant, so Dr. Ordway was called.

William's eight brothers and sisters formed a rather impressive reception committee for the immaculate Dr. Ordway who arrived promptly. After dispersing the youthful committee with a courteous rebuff, he passed quickly through the front door into the hallway where Mother was standing, her woolen dress covered with the inevitable Mother Hubbard apron.

"My boy's very sick, Dr. Ordway. You *must* save him. I can't let him go. I *won't* let him go!" Mother barked the anxious words like orders.

Dr. Ordway became annoyed. Mothers were always so much more difficult than patients. He frowned, thin brows digging a furrow in the middle of his forehead. "I'll do what I can."

" That isn't enough," she snapped, fixing indignant eyes upon him.

Coldly Dr. Ordway reminded her that " no doctor can do more," and turning went up the stairs to join the worried Dr. Huntley.

Mother was furious. Why do doctors treat human beings so coldly? One would think they were working with wax figures, they were that unconcerned. In her fear she could not understand the necessity for a doctor's objective attitude. Neither could Dr. Ordway fully understand Elizabeth Wanless' aggressive attitude. He couldn't know that her third child, little Willie, and fourth, James, had been taken from her at the same time in a diphtheria epidemic, and that she had named her next boy in their memory. He, the sixth child, was William James, and he held within him the future of her two other boys who had died. To her, William James meant more than one child . . . he personified three. And like a lucky omen, William James had been born the very year that America abolished slavery. " He's come into the world on the very threshold of its enlightenment," she often said and she meant for him to play a prominent part in its forward progress. That is why she clenched her fists and repeated over and over, " I can't let him die! I *can't* let him die! "

Lost in reveries, Mother didn't see her husband as he descended the stairway, his face grim and sad. He was wondering how to tell her. Dr. Ordway had simply said, " There is no hope." How could he repeat this to his wife? She looked up quickly, unexpectedly.

" What did he say? "

Father groped for words. If only he could comfort her first, then tell her easily, without so much hurt. But his face spoke before his words.

" John! " The cry was torn from her as she stared at him.

He tried to pat her shoulder. She shrugged him off. " What is he doing up there? Can't he help William? "

Father looked into her rebellious eyes. She'd inherited her rebellion from her mother, that grand young woman who had run away from the ancestral castle of her Irish titled father and romantically eloped with the coachman. Mother's eyes looked like fighting flints. A stray thought ran through his head. " Mothers fight for their young," he ruminated. " Fathers only mourn."

Mother's voice was insistent. " What did he say? " Father could only repeat Dr. Ordway's words, " There is no hope."

For a moment she seemed stunned, looked at him as though she hadn't heard. And then as he sank heavily into his scarred oak rocker, Mother whirled in fury.

" No hope? Who says so? A weak, human creature with a little black bag! How dare he say there's no hope! I don't care if every doctor in the world says ' No hope! ' He's my boy. He has a whole lifetime before him!" She gripped Father's hand. "The *Great* Physician hasn't said William must die! John, He can heal." Her voice grew husky. "Ask and it shall be given. Remember? Well, what's to prevent us from honestly believing that? I'm not afraid to ask for the life of my son!"

And Mother went into another room and asked. Not with formal prayers or petitions—not with Sunday worship phrases, but with weekday words, lifted right from her heart.

William's mother never knew how long she prayed, if one could call it praying, but she knew that suddenly her heart was light. There was no need to continue. William would live. All at once she was filled with joy; gladness seemed to leap within her. She always knew to whom to go in time of trouble.

As she started hastily up the stairs, she heard a great commotion. There was the sound of furious, hurried conversation; a ripping noise as if great pieces of cloth were being torn apart; the scurried tread of busy feet and then Annie rushed down the stairs, collided with her mother, almost knocking her down.

"Mother, upstairs quickly! Brother Thomas is here!" Annie darted away like a red-crested bird.

Mother wasn't surprised to learn that her eldest son was in the house. Her husband must have sent for Thomas when he thought William was dying. A completely ridiculous thought came to her. If only

William had been a chair, Thomas could have fixed him. Thomas, " the fixer."

As she came in view of William's attic bedroom, Mother gasped. A tub had been placed outside the unpainted door, a huge tub with a wringer attachment. A large boiler filled with steaming water was presided over by her tall Thomas who dipped large pieces of torn blanket into the steaming water, then passed them through the ringer.

Annie darted up the stairs and into the group. " Here's the bag filled with ice."

" Good," said Thomas, " we'll put that at the back of his neck."

Mother must have shown her bewilderment, for Father quickly stepped to her side. " Thomas thinks he can help his brother," and there was a small flame of hope kindling in the depths of his dark eyes.

" But what's all this? " queried Mother, pointing to the hot water and blankets and wringer.

Thomas greeted his mother over a cloud of steam. " How are you, Mum? " And with a gesture that included all the strange contraptions, he explained, " Hydrotherapy."

" What now? " thought Mother, and her eyes must have asked the question for her.

Thomas grinned. " This hydrotherapy treatment is something I picked up when Helen and I went to New York on our honeymoon. It fixes sick folks up fine." Thomas, " the fixer," whistled sharply as his fingers came into contact with the steaming water.

Mother felt Father's hand on her shoulder. "I've given Thomas permission to use the treatment on William." His shoulders straightened. "You were right. We must fight for him." And into his heart flowed some of the same fire and strength that had carried his own staunch Scotch father into the wilds of Canada with seven motherless children to give them liberty of conscience and freedom of worship.

For an instant Mother was rebellious. She'd prayed for William's healing and had received assurance in her heart. And now here was Thomas with his everlasting "fixing." She was about to speak sharply when it suddenly occurred to her that the Lord works through men. Why, this might be His answer to her prayer—God working through Thomas. Her face became calm and glad. Smiling, Mother stepped to the side of her tall, eldest son and started to work.

It was four, weary, steamy hours later that the members of the Wanless family made their way to beds and easy chairs, and relaxed with easy minds for the first time in five days. Every fifteen minutes for the past four hours, hot thick pads of blanket pieces had been applied to both sides of William's body. The small ice bag had been kept at the back of his neck. After four hours William's breathing had become easier, and he had dropped off into a quiet, peaceful sleep.

During his two weeks of recovery William became

rather thoughtful. He had been very close to death, and knew it. Never before had the world looked so promising. And there was a morning when the sound of a tiny brown bird singing in the window almost tore his heart with its beauty and reality. He had a lot of time to sit and think; to watch the chickens in the yard and the neighbors passing in the street and of life and his own relationship to it. What place should his life take in the affairs of the world?

Because he had been allowed but two visitors during his illness, he began to think of them. The doctor and the minister. The Rev. Mr. MacKay had always seemed like a pleasant old fellow who gave words of consolation to elderly women, but during his illness Rev. Mr. MacKay became an important individual to William. " He seemed to understand things," recalled the convalescing youth. " He talked to me about life and myself, about important things," he concluded. And the doctor. How important doctors were. A good doctor could bring joy out of near-tragedy. How sad it would have been for Mother if he had died. William blinked back the tears.

He should do something like that. He should make his life worth while! Now, which would it be—a minister or a doctor? Save bodies—or save souls? What was the verse Father had read him this morning? Oh, yes, about the disciples. Preach and heal. Preach *and* heal.

William sat bolt upright; clenched his hands together with fervor. He'd be *both!* A doctor *and* a preacher! Now, *that* was something to work for! *That* would be a career approved of God!

Over a cup of strong English tea and a crumbly scone, William made his announcement to his family and Rev. Mr. MacKay.

" I have decided," he said with quiet conviction, " to become a medical missionary." He looked about to see the effect of his startling words.

Brothers and sisters exchanged amazed glances; Mr. MacKay uttered a loud " amen," but Mother didn't seem in the least surprised. She just sat quietly, a smile upon her face, while her brimming heart flowed over and spilled from her eyes in tears.

While the Rev. Mr. MacKay's " amen " had been sincere, he was in no position to give William more than moral support. William's father was delighted with his son's choice of a lifework, but could give him little financial help, for there was a family of eleven to be supported with the earnings from the hardware store. So the task of financing his own education had been up to the youth from his moment of decision. But because it was a strong challenge—William answered it.

" Femur, Patella, Tibia, Fibula . . . bones of the leg. Now, what's the next one, Annie? " And the weary Annie who had promised to help her brother study Latin turned another page while the indefatigable William soaked up knowledge like a porous plaster far into the night.

" I'd suggest half-penny nails for pine wood, sir." William was working days at Father's store, giving excellent advice along with fair business practice while his once-small lump sum grew and grew.

" We must be of some use in this world. We must make something of our lives. We must give ourselves in service." It was William, filled with purpose and pep, speaking to the electrified members of the Dunn Street Sunday School class. Seven heads nodded agreement. Seven pairs of youthful eyes grew sharp with keen vision. Seven hearts beat faster and faster with a mounting desire to serve. Seven young men of William's Sunday School class went out into the field as missionaries.

William was not waiting until he was sent to the mission field. There was need in Toronto. He could help right now! " Jesus loves me, this I know, for the Bible tells me so. Now, let's sing the old song— everybody! " And two dozen scrubby, illy-clad youngsters shrilled out the tune for the wonderful young man who had organized a mission in a needy part of the city, and whose red-haired sister thumped away with spirit at an ancient reed organ.

Two years went by. The carefully-saved lump sum was of sufficient size to pay for his fare to New

York, entrance to medical school, a few books and a few meals. He could work part time, study the rest.

The beaming Sunday School superintendent at the Dunn Street Church, realizing their most promising pupil was to leave for New York in three weeks' time, chose the Sabbath lesson with great care. "The Good Samaritan," he confided to the Rev. Mr. Mac-Kay, "should prove of value and benefit to young Wanless, especially at this time." Young Wanless thought so, too, but was beset by an unexpected distraction.

Her name was Mary Marshall, and she had floated into the church, a creature in heavenly blue, just as the classes were departing for their different study rooms. William had a breath-taking glimpse of a pair of lovely grey eyes, a soft, sweet mouth and then the efficient superintendent took her in tow and directed her personally to the class of young ladies. William was unhappy. He had looked forward with real zest to the lesson today. Since his momentous decision of two years ago the Good Samaritan had been his favorite Scripture story, and there was no doubt the Sunday School had chosen it in his honor on that particular Sunday. But the words floated past his unhearing ears like a language unknown. His errant mind refused to dwell upon the Good Samaritan and instead persistently remained in a heavenly blue haze.

William's preoccupation was at first annoying to his teacher. The older man had expected a great deal

of response from young Wanless upon this particular
Bible story, and when faced with an expression distinctly out of this world, he was annoyed. But not
for long. "He's communing with things of the
spirit," the awed teacher said to himself, and continued the lesson in a quiet voice so as not to disturb
William's lofty meditation.

Eventually Sunday School was dismissed, but
William remained in his chair, bowed down with the
weightiness of this new problem. Heretofore women
had been divided into three classes for him. First—
mothers. Large, aproned, warm, capable figures who
led their families in a battle against dirt, starvation,
exposure, and frustration. Second—sisters. A
heterogeneous assortment of skirted figures who
shared the privacy of the home and giggled a great
deal. Third—other women. Those who were not
mothers and sisters but who simply formed a background for a world in which men did important and
interesting work. But now—here was a fourth class.
She was of the third division, and yet not of the third
division. For she was definitely not in the background, yet she intruded upon his thoughts. It was
obvious that this distraction couldn't go on. There
must be a way—a pleasant way of solving this new
problem.

The answer came very suddenly—and strangely
enough it had nothing to do with his ability to reason.
Being completely devoid of subterfuge William came

right to the point. As she floated out of the vestibule
into the foyer of the church, William spoke to her.

" I beg your pardon," he said, " but my sister and
I are having a Sunday School for some underprivi-
leged children over on Roncevalles Street this afternoon. Would you like to come and help us? "

Mary's eyes widened. " I'd love it," she trilled.

" Thank you," answered William. " That's a real
weight off my mind." And bowing he went into the
church and joined his family in their pew. He
usually listened attentively to each word of the sermon, but today a new thought ran through his mind.
" I must see if she'll take up nursing," he considered.
" A medical missionary's wife should be a nurse."
Wife! He blushed scarlet and tried to listen through
a rosy haze to the service. Mary sat with downcast
eyes for a whole hour, wondering why she had accepted this young man's invitation to help with his
Sunday School. " I'm going to see him this afternoon . . . this afternoon," her heart sang out and
she thought the sermon would never end.

Three weeks later, after a victorious and joyous
William had embarked for New York, Mary was ac-
costed over the dinner table by an irate father.

" What's all this nonsense I hear about you going
to take up nursing? " he demanded, his heavy, brown
moustache chopping up and down over a piece of
mutton pie.

" It's not nonsense, Papa. I intend to become a

nurse. Then I can be of help to William when he goes out on the mission field.''

'' Grrrph! '' Mr. Marshall adjusted his eyeglasses, fixed a grim look upon his daughter's lovely face. '' I think the whole thing is ridiculous! Ridiculous,'' he repeated, his moustache trembling like an animal about to pounce.

But Mary had won her greatest triumph and she knew this was simply a skirmish. The battle royal had occurred a few nights ago when she had accepted William. She had wisely asked that she be allowed to break the news to her father. His first reaction had been catastrophic. The world seemed to shake and heave upon its foundations and even the very elements seemed cowed. But gradually the eruptions subsided and now this was merely one of the minor after-quakes. Mary set her chin firmly and wished her father could see himself when he was angry. He looked exactly like the picture of an aged sea-lion which she'd seen on Annie's stereopticon.

'' It would be different if the young man had something steady, something stable under his feet. But this flighty missionary business . . .'' He dug into another portion of meat and ground it between well-cared-for teeth.

'' I'm sorry you don't approve my choice, Papa.''

He laid down his heavy silver knife and fork. '' I approve the young man. He's an excellent fellow. Splendid spirit. But this notion of his . . .'' Here Mr. Marshall removed his glasses, put them in their leather case. "Well, all I've got to say is that a visionary makes a deucedly valuable friend, and a mighty unsatisfactory husband. That's my advice. You may take it—or leave it alone."

Mary glanced primly at her father. "Thank you, Papa," she said.

"And another thing," he bellowed, furious that he was getting nowhere. "How do you know he's going to be able to take you with him? It doesn't sound like good business to me to send some weak woman traipsing off into a dirty, foreign country where she'd be more of a hindrance than a help. Now, if I were subsidizing a young doctor in a foreign field, I'd make it a hidebound rule that he should *not* take a woman along! And I'm not the only one who feels that way. You wait and see, young lady." And he felt considerably better, for this was a brand-new argument and one which Mary had not considered before. She looked troubled, a doubt had been planted in her mind.

Mr. Marshall smiled, plied his gold-plated toothpick with gusto, and felt pleased with the world

Mary's anxiety went into a letter to her fiancé in New York.

"Dear William," the letter began in the most delicate feminine handwriting. "Papa thinks there may be a doubt about my being able to go with you into the foreign field. What do you think about this, William?

" My nursing is proving very interesting, although somewhat different than I had anticipated. I scrubbed my first floor today so I am going to bed early tonight. You've no idea how tired I am.

" I would appreciate it very much if you could give me an answer to the above-mentioned question. Something rather practical that I could tell to Papa.

" Trusting that you are well and in good health, I remain your loving fiancée, Mary."

" Dear Mary," the letter was in masculine, bold handwriting. " You may tell your father that he need not worry. Our problems are all being taken care of and will be worked out to the utmost satisfaction of all concerned. They are in the hands of the Lord and He will provide. I trust you will excuse a hasty letter. This is my evening at the Bleeker Street Dispensary where I am gaining much valuable knowledge. Together with my school, dispensary work and the accounts I keep in order to pay my way, I have no time for mischief. I joyously anticipate the time when we will be together. Your loving William."

It had been six years since William had made his decision to be a medical missionary, and sister Annie, now twenty-six and still unmarried, was tying a blue bow on her sister Elizabeth's long curls.

" I want to see William," fretted twelve-year-old Elizabeth, whose long confinement in bed had made her nervous and irritable.

Annie soothed the thin little face. "He'll be here soon," she assured Elizabeth, trying hard to keep the tears from her eyes. The family knew that their little sister would never be well again. Mother prayed valiantly and the doctors came regularly, but Elizabeth's cough grew worse and her hands lay like tiny skeleton fingers on the gay patchwork quilt Annie had made for her bed.

"I have something for him," Elizabeth whispered secretively for the hundredth time. "Don't forget."

"I won't forget." Annie could be so patient and loving, for she was "big sister" to all.

There were voices below. A call. A dozen answers, then laughter and shouts of joy. "It's William!" cried Elizabeth. "It's William . . . William . . . William!" she piped at the top of her voice then started to cough violently and terribly.

Annie bit her lip. She did so want to be on hand to welcome William. She quickly poured a drink of water for her sister, soothed her, eased her, rubbed the worried forehead, the tiny arms. Presently Elizabeth was quiet. "I'll go tell William you want to see him," Annie whispered and went out of the room and downstairs where William's dear, familiar voice was booming out with exciting news. He had brought Mary with him, and as Annie looked into the two bright, eager faces she felt a deep surge of self-pity. She would never stand beside a man and know the thrill of stepping into life with him. The big, old house and the incessant demands of younger brothers and sisters seemed to be sucking her into a dark, cheerless future. She tossed her bright red hair, forced a smile, and went into the room to welcome her brother and future sister-in-law.

It was after Annie joined them that William answered their most pressing question. " Where will you be sent? " His answer created a complete furor. " I'm going to India," he announced proudly and the living room echoed with exclamations of wonder.

" When are you going? " " Who is sending you? " " Will Mary be able to go, too? " The youthful doctor felt as if he were in the midst of a furious examination.

" I'm being sent by the Bryn Mawr Church in Pennsylvania. That's in the States, you know," he explained.

" But how do they happen to be sending you? " queried the excited Annie.

As William settled back to tell of his good fortune, Mary watched him with fond eyes. William had said the Lord would provide, and He certainly did. How handsome her fiancé looked, Mary thought, as he told the family of his invitation to speak at the Pennsylvania church, and how dark his brown eyes became as he relived the stirring sermon he had preached about medical missionary work. But as he told of the church's interest in *him,* their decision to send *him* to India, the young man no longer remained seated, but buoyantly paced the floor.

Quite suddenly Mary was conscious of all eyes fixed

upon her. For William was telling of the generosity of the Bryn Mawr members and of their pledges sufficient to support not only a missionary—but a missionary and his wife.

As William told the story the family's delight became so infectious that Annie nearly forgot about Elizabeth, but a tapping from the upstairs bedroom served to remind her.

William was filled with nostalgia as he went alone into Elizabeth's room. He remembered when this room had been occupied by tall Thomas and John and himself. The same crack was in the windowpane, the same rag rug on the floor. His mother had made that rug, made it from her Sunday cape when it could no longer decently accompany her to church. In fact, Mother had worn it so long it couldn't decently accompany any of her daughters to church, even as one of Mother's inimitable " made-overs." So it was woven into a rug for the boys' room and there it stayed to remind childish feet that Canadian winters can be somewhat foiled by a mother's ingenuity.

" William! " Elizabeth held out her thin arms toward her big brother.

William stared, heartbroken. He wouldn't have recognized his own sister. Elizabeth had always had the reddest cheeks of any, and now her pinched face was colorless. William tenderly took her little hands in his, kissed her forehead and spoke with gruff tenderness.

" Well, it's good to see you! " he exclaimed, trying not to show his grief.

" I was afraid Annie had forgotten to tell you about me," Elizabeth pouted. " And I have something for you."

" Now, no. No presents," he insisted sitting on the side of her bed. " I want you to keep whatever you have for me and enjoy it yourself." William hoped his voice was jovial.

But Elizabeth's eyes filled with tears. " Oh, no! " She was greatly distressed, and pulled out a little cloth sack from under her pillow. " No, William, I saved this on purpose." And she opened the bag and painstakingly counted out the pennies—forty of them.

" There." She laid them in his hand with a smile.

" But, Elizabeth," William was deeply touched, " I don't want this for myself. You keep it."

" Well, it isn't for you . . . not *just* for you," she said, and then added in a practical voice, " You see—I want you to give it to children who need it more than I do."

For a moment William could think of nothing to say. Then he took the little cloth sack, filled it, put it in his pocket.

Elizabeth suddenly felt the gentle, tender arms of her brother holding her close; felt his kiss upon her hair, then his strangely hoarse voice whispered, " Thank you, dear. I'll remember."

Elizabeth's gift kindled inspiration in her older brother. "That forty cents has power to grow for *good*," confided William to Mary, and demonstrated his meaning by turning the small gift into eight hundred dollars before they sailed for India. Mary recognized, before William, his ability to raise money and watched with amazement the generous response of his audiences as he told church, Sunday-school and club groups of his sister's gift "For children who need it more than I do."

"That money will be used *only* for the children of India," William vowed. "No matter how badly it's needed for anything else—that's for the children. Elizabeth wants it that way."

Much to Annie's disappointment, Mary decided upon a simple wedding. There would be no attendants, no fussy clothes, no profusion of flowers. "But I wanted to make your wedding gown," protested Annie having visions of yards and yards of virginal white satin, great puffs of tulle and oceans of lace.

"I don't want any daughter of mine married like a common fisher-woman," blasted Mr. Marshall at Mary's mention of "simple wedding." "Everybody knows you can afford a big wedding, Papa," she soothed. "And there will be lots of people. It isn't that we won't invite our friends."

Mr. Marshall, an imposing, dignified figure in his cutaway coat and tall hat, thought of Mary's words as he entered the crowded Dunn Street Church for the marriage ceremony. " Everybody in town must be here," he muttered approvingly to William's friend, Bert Briggs, serving in the honored capacity of usher. As Mr. Marshall settled himself in the stiff pew he experienced the feeling of being in the midst of a large, devoted family. " This young man's well thought of, at least." He glanced toward the Wanless pew. Annie's swimming eyes conveyed a courteous greeting, while beyond her stretched the rest of the family—clean, upright, respectable. Mr. Marshall's stiffly-starched shirt front expanded. " Fine boy! Fine family! " he hissed loudly and at that moment decided to present his new son-in-law with the huge, gold Marshall watch.

" In sickness and in health, till death do us part." The rapt good-will of the wedding guests found reflection in the Reverend MacKay's benign face as he beamed at the two young people before him. Sister Annie was the only one who cried. Freshly laundered handkerchiefs had been carefully tucked into every pocket in the building, but guests found themselves smiling with joy instead of weeping.

" It was the strangest thing," declared the talkative Mrs. MacKay later, " but I couldn't set foot in that church for months without remembering that lovely wedding. It seemed to have a real spirit to it."

" It simply consecrated the building," added the wife of the Sunday School superintendent. " Simply consecrated that building."

William shook his head. The wedding and reception, the family, friends and even Canada were all behind them. He and Mary were in India now . . . face to face with Kali, the Goddess of Blood Sacrifice. Had William pampered his imagination he would have claimed that the fierce goddess leered at his two slender hands hungrily—eagerly. The young doctor shook off his reverie, helped his wife into the ghari and ordered the driver to return to the hotel.

"The train leaves for Sangli in less than an hour," he said, and was startled because his voice sounded strangely hollow.

❧ 3 ❧

WILLIAM WOUND his huge, gold Marshall watch and spoke above the noise of the heavy railroad car.

"According to schedule we should be in Sangli in ten minutes." He peered out into the dark Indian night which had fallen suddenly at eight o'clock without benefit of twilight.

Mary sighed. In ten minutes. That meant eight-thirty. She stifled a yawn and tried to find some new item of interest in the gaudy, busy pattern constantly before her eyes. The train was crowded even in their second-class compartment. She'd caught a brief glimpse of the third-class accommodations while boarding the train at Bombay's ornate Victoria Station two days before, and they reminded her of nothing more than cattle cars jammed with travelers, pilgrims, and India's assorted, ever-on-the-move population. The babble-babble-babble of female voices, the wailing of inevitable babies, the clatter-clatter-clatter of the wheels all formed a noisy, monotonous lullaby which threatened to put her to sleep. Even last night's stop-over at Poona had not rested Mary. She nodded. Brown bodies, red saris, gold jewelry, bright turbans, all ran into a delightful, blurred haze.

"Remember those wonderful mountains we came over?" murmured Mary to her husband.

" Not mountains, Mary. Ghats."

" Oh, yes. Ghats." William seemed eager to learn the Indian names and expressions. " The word ' ghats ' is applied to both mountains and steps descending into the rivers," he had painstakingly explained the day before. " The people think these mountains look like great steps, so they call them Ghats."

" Mmm," Mary had murmured, not as interested in his explanation as in the fact that their train had stopped to attach an extra engine to push them up over the steep Western Ghats.

There had been a brief stop at the top of the mountains.

" I've never been up in the air so high before in all my life," Mary had exclaimed and she felt as if her hair were brushing against the heavens.

" Look down there," William had directed, " if you want to know how high we really are."

She had felt a clutching sensation at her heart as they gazed into the valley far, far below. A soft shower had wiped the atmosphere clear, exposing a clear-cut miniature panorama of the surrounding country. " Those can't be people! " Wee, black, moving figures disturbed the quiet of the spreading grain fields below. William smiled. " Those are people, and *that* is a great, rushing river." He pointed to what Mary had described as a long strand of white embroidery silk, woven through the valley. The plains seemed to stretch interminably. " It's so

huge!" she had breathed. "And so grand," William
had added, vastly impressed.

"Sangli! Sangli Station!"

Loud, lively voices took up the call. "Sangli
Station!"

Passengers pressed toward the doorway, awkward
with possessions.

"We're here."

His repressed excitement was infectious.
"Sangli?" Mary's grey eyes popped open. Sangli.
The little dot on the map of India, a fingernail's
distance south of Bombay. "Three hundred miles,"
William had said. Mary stared out the window.
Who was there to meet them, she wondered. Where
were the missionaries with whom they were to spend
so many years of their lives? "I hope," she prayed,
"that somebody *will* be here to meet us." Her eyes
searched the strange figures on the station platform.
There were only some Indians loaded with bedding,
babies and food, ready to board the impatient train.

"Come, Mary, come!" William's arms were filled
with valises, water jug, umbrella and medicine bag.
Mary snatched up her hatbox.

To step from the crowded, noisy, odoriferous train
into the soft clean air of the Indian night was an in-
vigorating experience.

"Ooops!" They nearly collided with a vendor of
fruits. "Mango! Pamalo! Figs!" shrilled the
vendor, running alongside the train, peering into

open windows, a filled basket perilously balanced on his busy head. Natives from the third-class compartments shuffled off through the station. A freight-agent pushed a cart that squeaked like a frightened mouse.

" William, look at those people. What's the matter with them? " Mary pointed gingerly to large, cocoon-like figures strewn about the platform. Her obliging husband again gave her the benefit of his reading on India.

" Those are folks waiting for the morning train." he explained carefully.

" Well! " commented Mary as they picked their way among the carefree sleepers rolled up in dirty sheets, snoring away without a care in the world.

Just then a butter-yellow moon oozed up over the station roof, throwing a golden mohur tree into sharp silhouette. Mary caught her breath, touched William's arm.

" Look, the moon! "

Together they let themselves melt into the strange, tender beauty of the unfamiliar tropical night. " There's nothing like this in Canada," William breathed. She nodded. This beauty was too penetrating to form into words.

Another moon-shape appeared, this time in the form of an unromantic, brittle straw sailor hat.

" Well, Mary, it looks as though someone has come to meet us." This from William as the woman with the sailor hat drew near, her high-buttoned shoes with wooden heels clicking primly and precisely on the wooden platform.

" I suppose this is William and Mary Wanless." Syllables as prim and precise as the footsteps marched in orderly form from the mouth of their commander-in-chief.

" Yes, indeed," heartily rejoined William, and shifting his umbrella and medicine bag held out his hand to the woman confronting him.

Even the soft Indian moonlight could not soften the severe outlines of Victoria May Hastings. There were no loose hairs through which the light could form a halo about her face; no ruffles or frills to diffuse the severity of the shoulders or elbows; not even a feather or bow about her person to faintly suggest compromise with feminine desire for ornamentation. Victoria May was not only severe and prim, but she was plain and emphasized it.

As the sharp eyes stared at her pink bonnet, Mary felt suddenly overdressed. Her bonnet, which had appeared so simple in the presence of the enormous, bedecked hats of fashion, now seemed utterly frivolous, even riotous, while the blond curled locks took on the aspect of a Jezebel's coiffure.

" So *this* is Mary," stiffly commented Victoria May and Mary wished she could slink off into the dark night and reappear later in sackcloth and ashes, for she felt that nothing less could pass as commendable in the eyes of this rigid missionary from Sangli.

Victoria May's driver, a slender dark lad who had

taken charge of the luggage, now made his appearance.

"This is Rama," stated the missionary abruptly. "A fine, Christian boy." Her voice approved of him.

Rama acknowledged the introduction by making many salaams. As he looked at Mary he sensed a dampened spirit in the face of the pretty, fair stranger before him. Impulsively he departed, returning a moment later with a white flower which he graciously presented to Mary. "For the Wanless mem-sahib." His warm glance included both William and Mary. He thrilled as the flower gift caused the mem-sahib's lovely face to glow gladly in the silver-laced shadows.

As they seated themselves in the crude, buffalo-drawn bandi, Victoria May stared at William.

"Young man," she said, her eyes penetrating the night darkness, "you're younger than I had anticipated."

Mary's heart sank. This was a touchy point with William. What would he say? With relief she caught the twinkle in his eye. Then he jutted out his chin and Mary held her breath. Finally, after due deliberation, he spoke.

"Miss Hastings, I sincerely wish I could say the same for you."

A pause; a long, terrifying pause followed. Then, out of the corner of the bandi occupied by Victoria May issued a faint, gurgling sound. "She's choking

with anger," groaned Mary to herself, when the
sound became unmistakably clear. It was not anger,
but laughter. Mary shook her head. Her amazing
husband, with a few daring words, had completely
won the older woman—commanding both her interest
and her respect.

" Chee! . . . chee! " called Rama to the buffaloes,
twisting their tails and the bandi lurched out toward
the mission station three miles away.

Although the progress of the buffalo cart was slow,
because of the darkness little could be seen of the
surrounding country. It was all flat, flat land with an
occasional hut seeming to rise out of the earth and
fringed fields of wheat or millet. A few small babul
trees grew along the roadside. The darkness was
strange and still, broken frequently by the mellow
lowing of nearby oxen. Mary glanced at the sky.
The buttery moon and William seemed to be the
only ties she had with reality. It was suddenly comforting for her to think that this same moon shone
down on her matter-of-fact, sensible father snoring
loudly in his Toronto feather bed.

Surprisingly enough William and Victoria May
now chatted in a most friendly fashion. There was
so much William wanted to learn about the mission
station; about the native people; the work which had
been done and the work which needed doing.

" Well, you never want to be surprised at anything," Victoria May advised. " In my seven years
I've seen things to turn your hair grey. But the

Indian people themselves,—well, I love them! " She
blew her nose upon a spotless handkerchief. " I
intend to spend the rest of my days among them."

Mary wondered when William would tell about
Cora Stiger. After all, Victoria May had made the
arrangements for them to meet. But William seemed
intent upon learning of the work ahead of them.
" Well," thought Mary, " I'm sure he knows what
he's about. He really seems to get along with her
famously." She glanced a bit ruefully toward her
husband and this older woman, simply pouring conversation upon each other, and regretted deeply the
frivolous pink bonnet which had apparently made her
an outsider. " I'll dye it a dark brown," she vehemently promised herself. " An old, dirty brown.
And I'll bury this silly feather six feet deep in the
earth! "

William was telling now about their stop in Bombay; about the native bazaar, the immense Victoria
Station, their encounter with the helpful Parsee—but
nothing about Cora Stiger. Presently Victoria
May's eyes lit up. " She's going to ask now,"
thought Mary—and she did. She asked of Mary.

" How is Cora Stiger? You saw her, I presume."
The sharp eyes peered into Mary's.

" Well, yes," faltered Mary, wishing desperately
that William would take over the conversation. But
he was staring intently at a peculiar, roadside shrine
which could not be distinctly seen in the darkness.

" How is she? Well, I hope." Victoria May wondered why this silly, tongue-tied young woman couldn't answer even a simple question.

William cut into the conversation. "By George," he commented, still gazing out of the bandi at the small rounded object at the roadside, "what kind of thing was that we just passed?"

"That's a shrine to Ganesh."

"Ganesh? Ganesh?" William reviewed hastily his meager knowledge of Indian lore.

"Just one of their thirty million gods," commented Victoria May drily. "This one has an elephant's head and is supposed to be god of the harvest, among other things."

"Yes, yes. I recall now," beamed William. "Son of Siva, isn't he?"

"Something like that."

"I remember reading of him." William turned to Mary, eager to further acquaint her with the country's background. "Siva, you know, is the God of Destruction. One time he became angry with his son and cut off the boy's head."

"Oh!" The idea appalled Mary. "What terrible things they do in India," she thought.

"He did. But Siva's wife, feeling motherly, ordered her husband to replace their son's head."

Here Victoria May interceded. "Indian women don't *order* men about," she mentioned. "She probably groveled at his feet and wept."

"Anyway," continued William, "the father couldn't find the boy's head so he decided to cut off the head of the first living animal he saw and attach it to the son's body."

Mary's eyes were wide. " And the first animal he saw was an elephant? "

" Yes." William nodded approval. " That's why Ganesh has an elephant's head. However, I understand he's a jolly fellow in spite of it all."

" But what about Cora Stiger? " The prim maiden lady switched the subject abruptly.

Mary glanced at her husband. He was lost in his thoughts of Indian culture.

" William," her voice sounded thin, " Miss Hastings asked about Cora Stiger."

William looked at his wife in surprise. " Hadn't you better tell her? " he asked, considering news of a woman's death to be in the same category as births, weddings, showers and other information carried almost exclusively by females.

Mary felt her fingers grow icy inside the kid gloves. If she could only be tactful; think of some kindly, painless way in which to break the sad news to this woman about her friend.

" Well? " Victoria May's sharp voice became impatient. What was the matter with this young woman's tongue?

Mary squirmed under the other woman's impatience. There had been a school teacher once who'd possessed the same impatient stare. Mary had always felt stupid and tongue-tied in her presence, just as she was feeling now. Victoria May's high-buttoned shoe tapped impatiently on the floor of the bandi.

Mary felt helpless. "She's dead," she whispered and blushed with vexation and shame. I don't want to be cruel and hurt her this way, she thought.

Victoria May hadn't even quivered, but her face grew set and white in the moonlight. "Dead?"

Instinctively Mary reached out and touched the veined hands. "I'm sorry," she said, but Victoria May ignored her solace.

"Dead," she repeated, unbelievingly. "Cora Stiger dead."

"Tell her about it, Mary," directed William, unaware of his wife's inner conflict.

"You tell her, William," pleaded Mary. "I— I——" Her voice broke.

William grew most solicitous. "My dear, I didn't know it would affect you this way. Now, now . . ." and with a comforting word he gathered Mary's gratefully responsive fingers into his hand and proceeded to describe objectively and with much kindliness the death of Cora Stiger.

During this conversation the bandi had been drawing near a group of houses, well-lighted and bright from which issued sounds of merriment.

Suddenly there was a fizzy sound, then smoke and with a loud report a great Roman candle shattered gay colors against the background of black.

"Ohhh!" Mary's self-consciousness dropped away and her eyes lit up with excitement.

" Fireworks! " William exclaimed. " This *is* a royal welcome."

Fizz! Another great candle scattered light in the path of the oncoming bandi.

William could make out an archway in the road surrounded by excited, vocal people.

" Here they come! " " More fireworks! " " Come, quickly! " " They are here! " These and other words drifted out toward the road and spread excitement to the newcomers.

" Don't tell anyone else about Cora tonight," Victoria May requested. " I'll tell them later."

William nodded.

A half-dozen small dark boys, animated beyond the control of their mothers' restraining hands, dashed down the roadway shrilling, " Doctor-sahib! " " Mem-sahib! " " Salaam! Salaam! " Tiny hands threw bouquets of marigold and jasmine to the young couple while tiny feet stirred up more dust along the dry roadway, hazing their entrance to the mission compound and giving the whole picture a most unbelievable appearance.

An arch, curving over the gateway, was made of branches from the palm, banana and neem trees. On the arch, William could make out the word " Welcome," shakily spelled out in gilt-paper letters.

Festoons of gaily-colored tissue paper swung over the garden in front of the bungalow and glowed in the light of Indian paper lanterns.

" They've certainly done their best to make this a

festive occasion," murmured the pleased young doctor to his wife who squeezed his arm in excitement.

As the hulking buffaloes came to a stop, crowds of milling and delighted people thronged about the cart calling out their greetings, " Salaam! Salaam! "

Young men, pressing forward, helped the occupants alight, and Victoria May hurried the newcomers to seats on the verandah. Tiny flames leaped up from crude clay lamps. The plain rag wicks floating in oil caused a surprising thought to pop into Mary's mind. " These must be exactly the kind of lamps carried by the ' ten foolish virgins,' " she thought, then laughed. This Indian atmosphere was already prodding her active imagination.

With an expression as mellow as the moonlight, William looked deep into the faces of the people swarming before the verandah, and again he experienced the heart-warming feeling of India holding out her arms to him—pleading for healing, love and sympathy.

" Aren't you glad you came? " he whispered to his wide-eyed bride.

She nodded as two white faces approached through the dark-faced crowd. As they came onto the verandah Mary noticed that the man was slightly bald, heavily-spectacled, and walked with a limp. The short, stout woman with him could only be described as " motherly." Even in the midst of the exotic setting and in the glow of strange, crude lamps, she carried with her an aura of " Christmas at Grandmother's," " roast beef, mashed potatoes and apple pie."

Victoria May spoke. " Dora and Ezekiel Greyson," she announced. " My good assistants." To Victoria May everyone was her assistant, everyone with the exception of this newly-arrived young Canadian who immediately fell into the classification of co-worker.

Mrs. Greyson, puffing from her hurried trip across the compound, grasped their hands heartily. " My land," she said, and then William knew she was from America, " my land, welcome to Sangli, both of you! " Mrs. Greyson planted a hearty kiss upon Mary's cheek and turning to her spectacled husband, whispered, " Ezekiel, look at her. Pretty as a picture! " Mary blushed and the pink bonnet gained prestige in her mind.

" Glad to see you, young fellow! " Mr. Greyson pumped William's hand as William rebelled inwardly against the greeting. Unless he thought of some way to look older he would find it difficult to win the immediate respect due a doctor. Mr. Greyson turned to Mary, patted her awkwardly on the shoulder. " Mighty glad you came, too," he commented, thinking how pleasant it was to see a silly little bonnet over a pretty face.

Victoria May was motioning to them. " I think she wants us to sit down," said Mrs. Greyson, indicating chairs on the verandah. As soon as they were seated Victoria May turned to the natives milling

about the compound. " Quiet! Quiet, everybody! "
Her sharp voice drew immediate order from the
crowd. " You, too, Shanker." This to a mis-
chievous lad with heavy white teeth who was doing his
best to tease some little girls by pulling their braids.

" Ladies and gentlemen," began Victoria May in
her best platform manner, " we are gathered here
tonight to welcome to Sangli Mission Station two
dear young people from Canada—Dr. and Mrs.
William Wanless." Loud applause and cheers followed. The boy known as Shanker with the heavy
white teeth let out an ear-piercing whistle. Victoria
May raised her eyebrows and caused the whistle to die
in mid-air. She pulled down her shirtwaist and continued. " Dr. Wanless brings to us not only a
message of the Gospels, but his ability and training
as a doctor. I'm sure his work will be blessed as we
will be blessed by his presence in our midst." A
great round of applause indicated the pleasure of
the native people who eagerly anticipated Victoria
May's next words. " And now, in honor of our visitors, we will welcome Dr. and Mrs. Wanless with an
Indian custom, a pahn-supari."

This news caused a delirious reaction. Shouts of
approval rent the air.

" What's a pahn—pahn—what did she call it? "
Mary anxiously whispered into her husband's ear.

He pulled at his chin. " Pahn-supari . . .
Hmmm . . . I'm not sure, Mary. I didn't read
about that." He shook his head thoughtfully.

Mrs. Greyson noticed their bewilderment. She leaned over, tapped Mary on the arm. "It's an Indian party," she whispered, "where they serve pahn."

Mary nodded understandingly. So that was it. She smiled, winked her gratitude at Mrs. Greyson, then her brows furrowed. What in the world was pahn."

"Shiveramji!" Victoria May's voice rang out. "Will you please come forward?"

Up onto the verandah came a middle-aged man dressed in flowing white garments. Mrs. Greyson whispered again. "He's the leading man of our Christian community." William nodded his appreciation.

Shiveramji was followed closely by four young men whom Mrs. Greyson described gratefully as "all Christians."

"How lovely!" Mary exclaimed as the first young man approached carrying a large round brass tray piled high with garlands. "How good they smell!" Shiveramji lifted the most gorgeous one and placed it around Mary's neck. "Jasmine," said William peering at it closely, "strung with marigold and tuberoses." "Look!" thrilled Mary, "they're still damp."

William felt rather ridiculous when a garland was placed about his neck, also, but to judge from the ease with which Mr. and Mrs. Greyson accepted the same garlanding it was obvious that this was an accepted

Indian custom. Mary smiled at the incongruous combination formed by Victoria May's prim sailor hat and the large garland of gorgeous flowers about her neck.

The second young man approached, smiling shyly. He carried a little silver dish with a tiny cobra-headed spoon attached by a chain. "Hold out your hands," ordered Victoria May. "Take off your glove!" she reprimanded Mary. The young woman hastily drew off her left glove. "Your *right* hand," she insisted. Mary's eyes filled with tears. She felt bewildered in this new country. Dora Greyson leaned over as Mary removed her right-hand glove. "The right hand is for eating and ceremonial purposes," she explained. "Indians reserve the left hand for unpleasant duties." Mary sighed and nodded her thanks. Life was becoming dreadfully complicated. She held out her right hand. "Palm down," whispered Mrs. Greyson. Mary obeyed. The shy young man touched the back of her small white hand with the cobra-shaped spoon, leaving the pungent, spicy odor of sandalwood. "Doctor-sahib?" William held out his right hand, permitted sandalwood oil to be touched to his skin. The young native boy circulated among the missionaries, daubing the backs of their hands with the sweet-smelling fragrance.

Suddenly with no warning, the third young man stepped forward and brandishing a small, slender-nosed silver sprinkler deluged the guests and mis-

sionaries with showers of fragrant cologne. Mary
shrieked her surprise. " What a sweet shower! " she
thrilled and glanced toward her husband to see how
he was reacting. William managed to keep a smile
on his face, but he reeked with the flower scent. " A
pretty enough custom," he observed, " although I
must say I feel downright uneasy smelling like a
lady's boudoir! "

As Mary laughed at his discomfort a fourth young
man stepped forward, grim-lipped with downcast
eyes. He carried a brass tray heaped with something
that looked like round, green, lush worms. " Pahn,"
whispered Mrs. Greyson amused by Mary's revolted
expression. " You chew it." Mary's eyes grew big.
" Chew it? " she managed. Mrs. Greyson nodded.
Mary reached toward the tray, gingerly took one of
the green, worm-like concoctions between dubious
fingers. William picked one off the tray, then to
relieve their minds Mrs. Greyson took one, tossed it
into her mouth and smiled for she was an adept in all
Indian customs.

Mary nibbled experimentally, but William popped
his into his mouth and chewed with relish. " He
looks as if he's been waiting all his life for ' pahn,' "
thought Mary.

" Mrs. Greyson," William questioned curiously,
" what *is* this pahn? "

" Well," she smiled, " it's the leaf taken from the
betel-tree, smeared with a paste of slacked lime and
water, sprinkled with red powder and little pieces of

betel-nut. Then it's folded and fastened with a clove."

William sighed. "That relieves my mind, I can tell you!"

The Greysons laughed.

"When we first came to India," Mrs. Greyson glanced at her husband, "Ezekiel thought everyone had tuberculosis. It was a relief to learn they were only spitting 'pahn.'"

It was after midnight when the last well-wisher departed, leaving Mary and William exhausted.

They were in the bedroom of their bungalow. Mary gazed mournfully at the strangely high ceiling and the whitewashed walls so bare and dreary. "Will this ever seem homelike?" she wondered.

William pushed aside the imperative mosquito-net and sat on the bed. "Mary," he enthused, "I like India. I like the Indian people. We were certainly called to the right place."

As Mary turned around to speak, a long centipede came from under the bed and glided quickly across the matting and out the door opening onto the verandah.

"William!" With a shriek Mary scurried across the room and leaped onto the bed. She clung to her husband, wordless with amazement and fear.

"By George!" William finally managed to gasp. "That *was* a surprise."

She trembled so her golden hair fell down and

fanned out golden bright about her shoulders. " Do you suppose . . . do you suppose there are other centipedes ? " Her eyes were moon-size.

William picked up the kerosene lamp, looked down under the bed. " No more under here," he announced. " Probably just a stray one," he comforted. But she cringed. " Mary," he took her by the shoulders, " that's just a little of the seamy side of Indian life. There are lots of fine things about India. You wait, we'll enjoy it together."

Mary had stopped trembling and was gazing down at the floor. " William! This is the first place I've ever lived that didn't have a wooden floor! " she discovered. " Do you know we're walking right on the ground—except for this grass matting ? "

Her young husband neatly placed his unlaced shoes beside the bed. " Extraordinary people." His remark indicated that his mind was wandering from the physical aspects of their dwelling. " Their friendly, childlike spirit," he ruminated. " Their gentleness and generosity." He was on his stockinged feet. " By George, we can learn something from these people—just as they can learn something from us." He was beside her now.

Mary turned impulsively. " William, it's all so exciting. I feel as if I'm living in a different world! " She grasped his hands. " It's terribly strange, but it's fascinating, too."

William looked fondly into the freshness of her face. As he did so he discovered an unasked question in her eyes. She bit the corner of her lip, her eyes took on a bright, pleading expression. She'd worn that same look the day she had asked him to buy her the pink bonnet. Later he discovered the request had been premeditated. What had she been turning about in her mind this time? What quirks of imagination in that pretty little head?

" Well? " he asked. She might as well realize he could anticipate these questions.

Smiling, Mary looked up into his eyes. " William, when are we going to see the Taj Mahal? "

The Taj Mahal? Where did she learn about the Taj, he wondered. And then he remembered. It was among the amazing assortment of cards sister Annie had for her stereopticon.

" Oh, we'll see it one of these days," he remarked carelessly, carefully watching her reaction. Mary's face dimmed with disappointment.

" Don't *you* want to see it, William? " she insisted. Then in a small voice: " It's wonderfully romantic they say."

So that was it. In the back of her mind she had doubtless been planning for months to visit the Taj Mahal, the most romantic monument in the world. The Taj Mahal had captured in flawless marble what poets catch in words, what artists catch with paints, and what the ordinary mortal feels only at rare, exalted moments within himself. The exquisite tomb, built by the Mogul Emperor Shan Jahan in memory of his beloved wife, the beautiful Mumtaz-i-Mahal, symbolized romance for Mary Wanless. And she intended to see it with her adored William.

" When can we go? " she asked.

William pondered a moment. " As you know," he began profoundly, " we have been given one year in India to learn the language before starting work."

" I *know* all that." Then eagerly, " But could we go next week? "

" Next week? " William pretended astonishment. " Why, the Taj Mahal is way up in Agra. That's quite a distance from Sangli."

" Next month? " Her cheeks glowed pink. This meant so much to her. And a trip to Agra wouldn't cost much. They could learn more about the people of India on the way, and work hard on their language studies when they returned.

" William," with a pleading cry she was in his arms, " I want to see it while we're young. While we're happy. Someday—well, someday we may not have the chance to enjoy it."

William held her close. " You're not forgetting why we came to India, are you? "

" I know. We came to bring the Gospels—and your skilled hands. But before you're too busy, tied down to your work . . . before . . ." here she sobbed, ". . . before I become just a missionary's wife, let me be selfish! " Her tears fell upon his neck. " If we could only make it part of our wedding trip . . . it would give us just a little longer to be together—alone I mean . . . "

William tried to comfort her, but his mind was troubled. " Just a missionary's wife," she had said. He'd have to clear that up right now. " Mary . . ." he began.

She put her hand over his mouth. " Can we go? Can we go? " she pleaded.

He gently took her hand in his own; stared down into her face. " I tell you what we'll do." He tried to keep the twinkle out of his eyes. " We should spend a few days here in Sangli, getting acquainted, starting the language, and . . ."

" Yes? " breathlessly.

" And then . . ." he hesitated.

" Yes? "

" Yes. Then we'll go see the Taj Mahal—just you and I."

" Oh." She stared; it was too good to be true. Then with a cry of joy she was holding him tight, laughing out her happiness.

" Now, now, now . . ." He dried her wet eyes.

" I'm sorry for what I said," she apologized, " about being a missionary's wife, I mean."

" That's all right, Mary."

But words tumbled from her mouth. " It isn't that I'm not proud of you. Never think that. I am. I'm so proud of you and so happy to be your wife. Oh, we're going to do wonderful things. Just wonderful! "

" Yes, yes . . ." he tried to calm her. She was like an excited child.

"And goodness knows," she drew a deep breath, "there's plenty of work to be done."

"Yes," said William, on safe ground again. "But do you know what I think?"

"No. What do you think?"

"Well," he assumed a dignified air, "I think that there's absolutely nothing wrong with the Indian people that a good hot bath and the Gospels won't cure."

This struck Mary as being very funny and they both laughed heartily.

Like brass temple bells their laughter tinkled out over the still night air and warmed the heart of Rama, the servant-boy. Rama on his pallet in the *godown* was not asleep, for he was suffering with a sore foot that refused to heal.

"Tomorrow," he vowed, "I shall show my sore foot to this new Doctor-sahib." And for the first night in six months he went to sleep with a peaceful mind.

4

"BY GEORGE, what fine weather!" exclaimed William the next morning. "November—and it's like a warm summer day." He fastened himself into a cool white coat.

"The folks in Toronto are probably up to their ears in snow and ice." Mary examined her reflection in the small mirror and hoped her most severe shirt-waist would meet with Victoria May's approval. She glanced at her husband. A frown appeared on her face. "William, don't you usually shave before you finish dressing?"

A twinkle appeared in his eyes. "Yes."

"I thought so. Well, why didn't you this morning?"

He pulled down the white coat, glanced in the mirror and then made his announcement. "Mary, I'm going to grow a beard."

She stared in astonishment. "Oh, no. Surely you won't do *that!*"

He repeated. "I'm going to grow a beard and don't look at me that way because I mean it."

Her face distorted. "But you'll look so *old!*"

His smile was eager. "Do you really think so?"

"Yes."

"That's why I'm growing it." William fingered his whiskers. "Wait until these are full-grown.

We'll see if anyone ever calls me ' young fellow '
again.''

Before Mary could protest a gentle knock came at
the door. " Chota hazri," a soft voice called.

" Who? " William cast a quizzical glance at his
wife.

" Let's find out," Mary suggested. " Come in."

Slowly the frail door swung open. " Chota hazri,"
the voice repeated and standing in the doorway was a
graceful figure clothed in a white sari. She carried a
tray with tea and toast.

William stared. " What are you doing here? " he
demanded of the greying Indian woman. " Why did
you bring this? "

" I help mem-sahib." This with a nod and smile
toward Mary. " Me ayah . . . your servant," she
explained in faltering English.

A look of disapproval clouded William's face.
Turning toward the woman he spoke in a kindly but
firm voice. " Thank you, but we won't need your
services. Just leave the tray and we'll carry on from
here."

The woman looked bewildered. Tears came into
her soft, dark eyes. " I say wrong things? Sorry,"
she sobbed as she placed the tray on a low table.

" William, you've hurt her feelings." Mary
crossed to the weeping figure, put her arms about the
frail shoulders.

" You know I didn't mean to be unkind," he explained. " But we're not here to impose upon the

people. We are here to serve them. We didn't come expecting them to serve us."

" I don't think she understands enough English for me to explain," worried Mary. Just then the welcome sound of Victoria May's voice issued from the verandah.

" Good morning! " Victoria May's crisp tones were reputed to produce the effect of reveille upon late sleepers in the mission compound.

" A solution to our difficulty! " William strode to the door. " You've come in the nick of time," he welcomed her. " A minor crisis has arisen. Perhaps you can help."

Mary came out on the verandah, her arm about the weeping woman.

Victoria May was instantly on the alert. Difficulty between missionaries and natives must be avoided.

" What happened? " Her voice was brisk and businesslike.

William felt a bit uncomfortable at the heartbroken reaction of the ayah. " I only told her we wouldn't need her services," he explained.

" Why not? " snapped Victoria May.

" Miss Hastings," William began sternly, " my wife and I came to India to serve the people. We are not interested in making the people of India serve us. Mary is an excellent cook and can easily take care of what little housework we'll have." He folded his arms. " I'm not here to live as a lord but as a servant."

Had it not been for the sincere humility of William's voice, Victoria May would have laughed in his face. "Sitabai," she beckoned the servant woman to her side; spoke briefly in the Marathi tongue. Instantly Sitabai's face cleared. Tears gave way to smiles.

"Bring the chota hazri out here," ordered Victoria May. Sitabai nodded, then glanced back at the new Doctor-sahib with warm smiles of devotion and love.

"What did you say that cleared up the atmosphere so quickly?" queried William.

Sitting on the edge of the bamboo chair, cocking her head to one side, Victoria May resembled a perky chicken. "I merely informed her that the new Doctor-sahib was entirely well-meaning but fearfully ignorant of our Indian ways and customs."

William frowned. "Didn't you tell her that we were not planning to use servants?"

"I did. That's when she started to smile."

"By George," William paced the verandah, "I must say I don't approve of your customs."

Victoria May sat up spine-straight. "William Wanless, why did you come to India?"

William admired her directness. "To serve the people. To heal the sick and preach the Gospel."

"Exactly. Mary Wanless, why did you come to India?"

Mary felt as if they were in the midst of an examination. "Why, to help William," she answered.

"I thought so. Now, how can you do it if you

spend eighteen hours a day with the household tasks?"

"But it won't take ——" Mary began. She was interrupted.

"But it will! Surely that prospect doesn't appeal to you."

"It sounds as if you're accusing my wife of gross inefficiency," retorted William, irritated by her attitude.

"I have no doubt as to your wife's efficiency as a nurse." The older woman drew a deep breath. "But as to her ability to haggle for hours in native bazaars, to carry drinking water on her head from distant wells, to cook over open fireplaces and wash your clothes by beating them on the rocks in the river, I have my deepest doubts."

"What do you mean ' haggle in bazaars '?" asked Mary, mystified by this strangely opening picture of domestic life in India.

"There's no such thing as a price tag here," Victoria May explained. "I can imagine you, young woman, with no knowledge of the language, trying to buy even a bunch of grapes, let alone all the food necessary for your meals. It takes an experienced Indian shopper three to four hours a day prying food out of the bazaar-wallas. They would charge you exorbitant prices and unless you were careful your month's salary would be gone for food in one week."

William made what he hoped was a constructive suggestion. "Why can't something be done about

that?   Now, if these people knew about price
tags ——''

Victoria May folded her bony arms. '' There is so
little time, and so much to do. Let us be concerned
with essentials.''

As they sat on the verandah and enjoyed the hot tea
and toast, the older woman continued to explain.
'' I've arranged for your other servants, also.
They're all fine, trustworthy people.''

'' Others? '' William's surprise flashed in his face.
'' Can't *she* manage things? '' His gesture was directed toward the retreating Sitabai.

'' Surely you've done some reading about ' caste.' ''
Victoria May was not used to having her remarks
pried into so completely.

'' Of course.''

'' Then you should realize that the woman who
cooks your food would never condescend to sweep the
floor. While the person who sweeps the floor would
rather die than debase himself by carrying away the
refuse. And so it goes all down the line. Your Hindu
tailor would no more contaminate himself by sewing
on a piece of leather, than you'd fall down and worship Ganesh, the elephant-headed god.''

'' But the Christians,'' insisted William. '' Surely
they don't continue to recognize caste.''

'' No! '' Victoria May replied emphatically.
'' They do not! ''

'' Well? '' The question was a challenge.

For the first time since they met, Victoria May

lowered her eyes and sighed. Mary noticed how weary her body seemed to become under the stiffly-starched white dress. " There are not," she admitted sadly, " many Christians."

Mary's heart went out in sympathy to this hard-working woman who had toiled to win souls for so many years, and who summed up her net results with the pathetic words: " There are not many Christians."

But William wasted no time with regrets. Crossing to Victoria May he touched her arm encouragingly and with a firm voice boomed out his promise.

" There may not be many now—but there will be ! "

Unknown to the occupants of the Doctor-sahib's bungalow, a bedraggled crowd had been straggling into the compound since early dawn. Running noses, sore eyes, faltering footsteps and blind-staring proclaimed their bodily ills, while their ragged clothing and unwashed bodies marked them as villagers of pitifully low caste.

Naked babies clung stickily to soiled mothers who sat in the dust, side by side with lank men wrapped in loincloths and turbans. Little rag-bags of children squatted in imitation of their elders, trying to curb childish impatience. A movement passed through the tattered group like the wind through green fields of millet.

" Doctor-sahib," came a faint wailing.

" Doctor-sahib ! " " There he is ! " Excited whispers announced the doctor's appearance on the verandah.

" Doctor-sahib," moaned suffering voices.

Mary was the first to see them. Instinctively her heart contracted and she felt cold. " William and I are going to see the Taj Mahal! We *are!* " she insisted to herself, not knowing the reason for her sudden panic.

" I suppose you plan to start your language study immediately? " Victoria May was saying as she started down the verandah steps.

" Immediately," verified William.

And then the older woman caught sight of the squatting natives. " Good gracious! " She swept them with a penetrating look, then addressed an aged man in the native language.

" What do you want? "

" Missi-sahib, we are sick," he quavered. " We heard that a doctor has come."

" What did he say? " eagerly asked William.

Victoria May repeated the ancient's remarks. William searched the faces before him.

A coughing old woman cried out, " Doctor-sahib," in a voice which quavered like the wail of the paddy bird. Her thin hands fluttered toward him in supplication.

William was touched. Like helpless, pitiful children they had come to him to be made well. No skepticism, no questions. He could cure. Faith burned in their eyes.

" But I'm not prepared to practice," he said to Victoria May. " Tell them."

She nodded, was about to speak when Rama's figure appeared from the side of the bungalow where he had been listening.

" But we are sick! " He spoke impulsively.

Surprise brushed Victoria May's face. Rama sick. Why hadn't he told her?

William's glance included the young man as he explained further. " You see, I have no money and no equipment. I was told to study the language for a year before starting my medical work."

Victoria May explained to the group. But they didn't move; just stood with wide, pleading eyes.

William became firm. " It's impossible for me to be of help right away. I have only my bag of meager medical supplies. I'm not equipped to practice." He looked analytically at several of the natives. " Most of these people need hospital care. I'm sorry."

As his words were translated William expected to see some resentment, some glances of animosity, but instead he saw only mute, sad expressions of silent suffering while the people raised themselves from the ground and shuffled out of the compound, down the road. The patient suffering of India gripped the doctor's heart.

" Rama! " Victoria May's voice caused the boy to turn.

" Yes, Missi-sahib? "

" What's the matter with you? You didn't tell me

you were sick." Her concern for one of her tiny band
of native Christians took the form of a scolding.

Rama's face was expressionless. " Doctor-sahib
cannot treat us," he answered, and with the expressive, fateful shrug of the shoulders he turned away.
William noticed the boy's slight limp as Rama attempted to protect his left foot from firm contact
with the ground.

During the exploratory day Mary made the most
of every opportunity to lift the brooding, preoccupied
look from William's face. They explored the missionary compound, enjoyed an elaborate breakfast
with the Greysons and met the two Greyson children,
Daniel, an impish ten, and Cecelia, an embarrassed
thirteen. The afternoon went by quickly with a visit
to the mission school with its score of little brown
pupils. Here both Victoria May and Mrs. Greyson
took turns daily teaching English, sewing and the
Gospels, relieving the Christian schoolmaster who
taught only in his own language, the Marathi.

Later that evening as she watched the tropical
moon throw magical shadows on Victoria May's hair,
Mary felt a vague uneasiness in her heart. She could
hear William inside the bungalow as he unpacked
their trunk. She had tried all day to lift the troubled
look from his face, but had not succeeded. Perhaps
tomorrow. Mary stirred in the verandah chair,
turned her attention to Victoria May who had leaned
toward her confidentially, about to speak.

" You can never be too careful about cobras."

Mary twitched. She had tried all day to forget about that centipede of last night. And just as she was settling down into the magic of the Indian night, Victoria May prepared to embark on such distasteful subjects.

" Their favorite spot is the bathroom." The older woman's face was severe. " You see, it's dark and cool there. Why, I've found them under the tub several times."

Mary shuddered.

" I have! " insisted Victoria May. " And remember this. Never walk anywhere at night without a light or torch." She straightened her shoulders. " One bite and you're gone! "

Mary bit her lip. " I believe she enjoys trying to scare me," she thought, but remained in an attitude of attention.

" Now, about the lizards." She galloped off into another disturbing description. " They hide behind pictures on the wall and dart out any old time to catch flies and spiders. They're not poisonous, but sometimes their incessant chirping is enough to drive you crazy." Another thought occurred. " Oh, yes! Whenever they're frightened they drop their tails." She waited for the effect of this statement. It registered. Mary gulped, blinked her eyes. " Yes, indeed," the prim one nodded emphatically, " India's a great stiffener for jumpy nerves! "

Mary heard her own voice quiver out, " Thank

you, Miss Hastings, for telling me these things. I'll
try and remember—about the cobras.'' She smiled
with what she hoped was assurance, but her mind
whirled. '' I'll never get used to cobras . . . never,
never, never. Every time I go into that bathroom . . . ! '' She stopped thinking about it. '' I—
I believe I'll go inside if you don't mind.'' And saying good night, she hurried to join William. There
was something about William's presence that made
cobras less frightening.

'' William.''

He didn't answer. Slumped deep into a chair the
doctor stared at his medicine bag.

'' William! '' That peculiar fear gripped her
again. Why was he so troubled? Why couldn't he
forget the natives who had wanted help?

He turned. Mary dropped on her knees beside his
chair. Tucking her arm through his, she smiled.
'' You know,'' she squeezed his arm tightly, spoke excitedly, '' I can hardly wait to see the Taj Mahal.''
Her eyes grew pleading. '' Can you? ''

For William the picture of the ancient tomb had
faded behind the pressing, pitiful needs of the morning's sufferers. Yet he was not equipped to be of
help, and it was really useless to worry about something beyond his control.

So smiling down at his wife he answered brightly,
'' Yes, my dear, I can hardly wait to see the Taj
Mahal.'' As he kissed her fingers she felt certain that
the shadow had lifted from his heart.

Bright morning again. Their second day.

" Doctor-sahib . . . Doctor-sahib! " anguished, suffering voices called out. Again a crowd of sick squatted before the verandah. But today there were more than yesterday.

This time the swollen crowd included a worried young mother who held upon her hip a fretting baby with sore, swollen eyes. Dirty, foul rags bulged over festering arms and legs of men, young and old. An aged one hacked and coughed, while a small boy nursed his discolored jaw. Others in their rags looked starved and ill. This time Rama stood near the group.

" Doctor-sahib . . . Doctor-sahib," the thin voices wailed.

" Rama," began William rather desperately, " you must tell these people to go away. I explained yesterday that I have no medicines to give them. It will be a year before I can start my practice."

Rama's face was sad. " The sickness, it will not wait a year."

William groaned.

Mary's heart grew faint as she looked upon an elderly man whose face was hideous because of staring, empty eye sockets.

" Doctor-sahib," he whispered over and over again. " Doctor-sahib."

" You must tell them," insisted William. " I have no medicines."

" You *can* have! "

The voice came sharply from behind his shoulder. William turned, puzzled, and met the eyes of Victoria May. She explained. " Medicines and surgical instruments are available in Bombay."

Excitement burned in William's eyes. " But the money? "

Her thin lips smiled. " Mr. Greyson can tell you about that." And with a quick gesture she motioned the hesitant, bespectacled Ezekiel Greyson from an obscure corner.

"Well, Dr. Wanless," he began timidly, " we have a small fund in the mission that we've been saving for an emergency." He cleared his throat, grinned. " This, we think, is that emergency! "

Victoria May bobbed her head as Mr. Greyson pointed to the group of sick squatting on the ground. " Tell him why we think so," prompted the wiry woman.

" Yes." The timid voice grew bolder. " These low-caste Indians are in right desperate need. In fact, that's why we wanted a doctor to come here. You see," his glasses fogged up with his intensity, " there are thousands and thousands of villages and not one doctor! Only quacks and sorcerers who try to drive out evil spirits and devils with the most heathenish kind of torture! " The timidity was gone. Mr. Greyson launched out eloquently. " Your practice is ready and waiting, Doctor! And if you want to start your medical work now, our emergency fund is at your disposal! "

"And you can study the language in the evenings," postscripted Victoria May.

William, speechless at this unexpected offer, glanced from Mr. Greyson to the pitiful sufferers before him. Spellbound, he began diagnosing from a distance.

"William," Mary began faintly, "William, have you forgotten?" The Taj Mahal was swiftly fading. These sick natives were becoming the reality. She must bring his thoughts back.

"Eh?" replied William in response to her words.

"The Taj Mahal," she whispered and waited with eager heart.

Victoria May's ears were sharp. "What's this about the Taj?" she wanted to know. Mary resented the intrusion. Summoning up her courage she faced the older woman boldly. "My husband is taking me to see the Taj Mahal," she announced, surprised at the courage in her voice.

"Oh." Only one word, but in it was the scorn of the strong for the weak; the contempt of the dutiful toward the dreamer; the antipathy of a plain, unwanted woman toward a wife with beauty and charm. Victoria May turned abruptly. "It's your decision, young man," she snapped and departed with Mr. Greyson trailing in her wake.

There was silence. The native sick, sensing a crisis, huddled staring with desperate hope and fear. Mary said no more, but in her mind tumbled picture after picture of the marble-white Taj, the quiet lagoons which mirrored its beauty, she and William, young and happy, enjoying its loveliness. She and William, young and happy. . . . Oh, William, she breathed to herself, while we're young . . . while we're young. Her beautiful eyes pleaded with him, urging, urging.

William passed a hand over his troubled forehead. He had not known such conflict before. His path had always been clear-cut—the way obvious and straight ahead. He sensed the importance of this decision. He knew the conflict was age-old to man. Duty pitted against pleasure.

His duty was obvious. He had come to India to heal. Here were his patients. The way was open.

But he was young. His past four years had been devoted to study and hard work. There had been so little courtship—such a short period of joy and happiness away from duty. Each moment was precious. More moments were stretching forth their enticing fingers toward him. He was young . . . Mary was so beautiful.

William sighed—and looked into the eager eyes of his wife.

" Mary . . ." His eyes held promise.

" Sahib! " Rama's anguished voice broke the spell. " Sahib, my foot! " And with haunted, fearful eyes, Rama held up his foot for the doctor to see.

William had to look. The boy was right beside him.

" Why is it sore, Doctor-sahib? " The boy's anxiety broke into beads of perspiration on his shining, brown forehead. " Why? "

William's voice hit a serious note. " Rama, pull up your shirt," he directed. " Let me see your back."

Rama obeyed, wondering.

The doctor looked at the exposed back flecked with the telltale spots.

" Can you feel this ? " He pricked one spot with a pin.

Rama shook his worried head. " No."

William pulled down the thin shirt. Rama turned, his face tense. " Sahib ? " The question was torn from his throat.

William looked into the handsome brown eyes—the eyes of one doomed to die suffering and horribly. Rama was a leper.

" Come," said William, and with his arm about Rama walked down into the crowd of sick and suffering. " Tell these villagers I will do what I can for them."

And Mary stood on the empty verandah alone, her dreams of the Taj Mahal becoming as vague and fleeting as the white, white clouds overhead in the sky.

5

"Doctor-sahib . . . Doctor-sahib," the pitiful wail never ceased. Hour after hour, day after day, the steady stream of sick and suffering filled the mission compound. Day after day, hour after hour, diagnosis, prescriptions, medicines, operations.

To commemorate the first anniversary of their arrival in India, Mary's stiff, marbleized-paper scrapbook carried the following words:

"It is just one year ago since William and I arrived, lurching along in that bone-cracking bandi driven by Rama. Poor Rama. William's doing the best he can but the disease is so loathsome and apparently incurable.

"If our first year in India had been according to my planning I could have written in this space a description of the Taj Mahal. But now something more important can be entered here. In the short space of twelve months, in which I would have had us traveling about seeing the sights, William has treated seven thousand sick people. I don't imagine many doctors back home have seven thousand patients their first year of practice. He says he thinks that if he had stayed in Canada he would probably be sitting in an office still waiting for his first patient. But then, William is the only medical man in all this part of India.

" There are no other missionary doctors here and the few British doctors in India are in the cities. The latter don't want to live in the primitive, unsanitary villages so the village population just suffers or dies.

" No wonder the people come in crowds for medicines. And the operations William performs! Everyone thinks they are miraculous. And so do I. And to think he had absolutely no equipment with which to start. For an operating theatre he uses our little six by ten bathroom, and he made his own operating table out of the packing boxes that brought our goods from Canada. I don't suppose any doctor ever started out with less.

" Whenever he needs something he uses his own two hands and builds it. And the dreadful diseases! I'm sure William couldn't have studied about many of them in a New York medical school, but he never hesitates. He does his best—and is usually successful. The people are *so* grateful. One Hindu woman, recovering from an operation, called him ' The Doctor-sahib with the miracle-hands.'

" Right now he's moving the dispensary from the mission compound into the town of Sangli. In the first place we haven't enough room, and the second reason is because the school children have become so curious to see what is going on that they are a nuisance. They peek in the windows, they crowd around the door, they dart in and out among the patients making more noise than monkeys. Everything considered, I'm sure we'll do much better work in this new location. We plan to continue living in the mission compound even though the new dispensary is in town."

Mary read over her words. " A new dispensary in town." She smiled. It sounded so elegant, when in reality the new dispensary was made from a dilapidated, abandoned shack, a place of refuge for donkeys.

She remembered the puzzled attitude of the donkeys when they had returned to their haven. A door barring their entrance had caused them a great amount of frustration. They couldn't understand that their old shelter was now a dispensary.

" It's the only place in town for rent," William had regretted, and at first it had seemed as if he was not to be permitted even the use of the donkey shed. While millions of Indians needed medical care, native authorities were afraid of the new medicines and methods. " We have our ancient cures," they protested. " We do not want your poisons." But William persisted and one day found himself starting the work of remodeling.

A door was hung and glass put in the windows. After lengthy arguments and pay in advance, coolies lazily leveled the undulating dirt floor by pounding it with heavy posts. Then to keep the dust from arising, the floor was finished native-fashion: smeared with a paste made of cow-dung and water. A ceiling was made with strips of white muslin.

William brought his rough-board operating table

The Shack Dispensary.

and medical shelves from the compound and completed the furnishings with a desk and three chairs.

The day the remodeled shack was open to patients William had chortled, " By George, I wouldn't be ashamed to treat any rajah here! " And then he and Mary had laughed at the very thought of any wealthy Indian potentate remotely considering treatment at the hands of a Christian doctor in an ex-mule shed.

" Anyway, we're in distinguished company," William observed glancing out the window of his dispensary. Mary followed his glance. At the roadside grew a large neem tree, sacred to Hindus, beneath which an exorcist sat most of the day. Like tiny butterflies, bits of bright rags with charms fluttered from the neem's low-hanging branches. A patient approached. With a quick incantation the exorcist grasped one of the branches and waved it frantically over the squatting patient. The rags flapped like wings in flight. The treatment was over. Leaving his fee the patient departed.

" That's the easy way," commented William as he and Mary went into the yard to watch the slow building of an open shed. Its jungle-grass roof would offer protection to patients who could not return to their own homes, but little else. No beds, no blankets. Only overhead protection.

Jokingly William called this shed his " fresh-air ward," while his heart yearned for better accommodations. However, he reviewed his tiny staff with a degree of satisfaction: Sugandrao, a swarthy and impulsive young compounder from a government hospital who was secured to mix the powders and medicines; Mary, who was an efficient and capable nurse; while he, himself, attended to all diagnoses, prescriptions and operations.

On a rainy day disaster nearly overtook William.

" Hold that umbrella steady," he ordered taking strong, sure stitches in an operation for leg infection.

Mary's arms ached. Fully five minutes ago, at a most inopportune moment, the roof had started to leak.

Drip, drip, drip, came the raindrops, splashing merrily upon the chloroformed patient.

" Do something! " William had roared, and she had snatched up an umbrella, holding it in a position to deflect the water.

Heartily discouraged with the makeshift dispensary, Mary doggedly kept the umbrella aloft with the firm belief that she knew exactly what the upraised-arm holy men went through to attain their postures of distinction.

" Someday we'll have a real hospital," William said later as he and Sugandrao rebuilt the ragged grass roof with substantial tiles from the village.

" Do you really think so? " Mary's eyes reflected her concern.

William smiled. " Don't you have faith in your husband? " he asked.

" It's the same old problem," she replied. " If we can't attract anybody except outcastes there won't be money to build a hospital."

William was thoughtfully silent. She had hit upon the most difficult task of all, this breaking through the caste lines. At first he had found it hard to believe that high caste Hindus would rather endure suffering than submit themselves to the ministrations of a Christian doctor. But although he had treated seven thousand Indians, he had yet to treat a high caste man.

Less than a week after William had repaired the roof, the sound of horses' hooves on the road caused Mary to peek curiously out the door of their dispensary.

" Don't be afraid, son, I won't hurt you." William's kindly voice soothed the ears of his youthful patient, as his equally kind hands removed a filthy bandage from a festering sore.

Mary turned from the door in excitement. A bright, spangled carriage had stopped in the road, and now native servants emerged clearing a path through the squatting, patient sufferers around the door. When it became apparent that the occupant of the carriage would not suffer contamination by contact with any of the inferior ones before him, he alighted and came toward the crude dispensary, rich brocades sparkling in the sunlight.

Her crisp uniform crackled with delight as Mary whispered, " William, a rich man at last! "

Her husband smiled at her words. "You mean wider recognition, don't you?" he asked as she smoothed down the white uniform, tidied her hair.

The beggar lad, whose festering arm William was examining, instinctively drew back as the high caste man approached.

"Did I hurt you?" queried William in slightly imperfect but understandable Marathi.

"No, Sahib," muttered the lad and gestured timidly as the proud figure loomed in the doorway.

Immediately William sensed a crisis. This man, as warranted his position and caste, expected immediate attention. The doctor would be expected to turn from his examination of a lowly beggar lad and serve the newcomer.

"Dr. Wanless?" The visitor's speech was clipped and studied.

"Yes," William answered courteously.

"I am not well. I have been told you have miraculous hands, so I have come to you for help."

"I shall be delighted to do what I can for you." William hesitated, realizing his next words would formulate policy for his dispensary and any future hospital. Should he treat this high caste man now, or ask him to wait?

"Yes," he said amiably, "I'll be glad to help you." Then added, "But I must ask you to wait your turn."

Mary held her breath as the proud figure turned and looked out into the dispensary verandah and beyond. He saw only miserable creatures whose very shadows were contaminating to one of his caste. Facing William he spoke stiffly. "There are none before me."

Mary, rather alarmed, kept in the background, but William rose to his feet, his eyes growing deep and warm as they did when faced with conflict. "My friend," his voice was calm, "I have come here in the name of Him who preached brotherhood. You are my brother, but no less nor no more than those whom you call untouchable. When I use His power to heal you, I cannot repudiate His word. I will help you, if you await your turn."

The eyes of the proud, erect man grew bright and fierce. Staring into William's calm face, he uttered one word. "Christian!" The word hung in the air like a curse, and the richly clothed figure strode to the carriage and drove away.

"Sahib! Doctor-sahib!" The beggar lad was weeping. The wrath of the high caste Hindu had frightened him.

Mary looked at William as much as to say "What have you done?" but the question died on her lips as she looked upon the rejected but brightly victorious face of her husband.

Several weeks passed, and the rains started to come, but every day regardless of weather, the little dispensary was crowded with India's multitudinous sick. "And this," said William to his wife, "is only in and around the small town of Sangli. Imagine the work to be done in *all* India.'' But it was like trying to conceive of the distance to the nearest star.

'' Who's next? ''

William depended upon Mary to keep the patients in line. Mary guided a very old, blind man into William's hands.

'' Eyes,'' she murmured as a commotion sounded from outside. The noise of horses' hooves beat upon the road and for the second time the elaborate carriage of the proud Brahmin stopped before the little Sangli dispensary.

Mary immediately started to worry. '' Maybe he's come back for vengeance,'' she gasped, expecting to see a revengeful individual emerge from the carriage with a sharp, drawn sword and an evil look in his eye.

As they watched, the richly-dressed Brahmin stepped from his carriage, dismissed his servants and entered the dispensary gate. Mary strained, but she could see no sword, the man moved without anger. Then suddenly, instead of striding toward the dispensary, he moved quietly into the courtyard and humbly awaited his turn behind those whom the white doctor had called '' brothers.'' He had come back for treatment—under William's terms.

The young doctor felt himself trembling. The spirit of good-will was at work, penetrating, reconciling, reaching into the heart of this haughty man. Soon there would be others. Because of the expression on his face, Mary expected a torrent of jubilant words. But William made no comment. He was carried away in the anticipation of a time when the ancient system of caste would totter; when the people of India would know brotherhood.

Days stretched into months and months into seasons. For William time had no meaning. Each day was the same as the one before. From eight until twelve the diagnoses and prescriptions, and in the afternoon the operations. After that the visiting of the sick and the innumerable demands which made time as fleeting as the smoke from a funeral pyre.

" Report for the year," dictated William turning up the wick on a kerosene lamp. " Patients—7,000."

Mary bore down on her lead pencil. " I have it," she announced. " And please give me the figures of operations carefully."

William consulted his hospital notes. " Abdominal, one hundred and six."

" Yes."

William smiled fondly at the earnestness of his wife as she bent over a small pad of paper. " Er— abscesses, sinuses and fistulae, ninety-three. Amputations ——"

" Too fast," cried Mary writing at top speed. " Ninety-three. Amputation? "

" Twelve."

She looked up quickly, wetting the tip of the pencil with her tongue. " Does that include your crutch-patient? "

" Crutch-patient? " he asked, then smiled for her

remark had reminded him of an ingenious bit of handiwork which saved the life of a hearty Indian youth. " Save my son, oh, save my son," the ancient, shriveled father had pleaded as he staggered into the Sangli dispensary. " I have come far, my son is dying," gasped the aged one as William hurried to the ox-cart to see a young man writhing in agony. It was obvious that they had been traveling many days, and it was also obvious that the youth was in a critical condition. " Gangrene," William thought, as he looked at the crushed and putrefying leg of the boy. " We'll have to amputate his leg immediately," he told the father. A look of astonishment came over the wrinkled face. William explained. " We must cut off his leg to save his life." This declaration had been followed by a vigorous shaking of the head. " No, Sahib, no. A boy is no good with just one leg. He must work in the fields." " I'm sorry," the doctor replied. " It's his leg or his life." There had been a moment's pause, then the old father spoke. " I will take him home," he murmured and started to leave. " But he'll die," William warned. The ancient one shrugged his shoulders. " Better a dead son than a crippled one. He will not be able to earn his food. I shall have to work for him." As the father started away William had caught the eye of the youth. " I am young," the boy's expression seemed to say. " I have so much life before me. Do something for me, Doctor-sahib." And before he even gave it another thought, William called out impulsively, " Stay! I

will see that your son has another leg!" Another
leg? The old father's face froze in disbelief. This
was too much magic. "He shall be able to help you
and will be able to walk," promised William to the
skeptical one. The youth's face burned eagerly but
the father shook his head. "It is not possible."
William took a firm grip on his patience. "Isn't it
better that your son be alive with an artificial leg than
dead?" The old man chewed on his fingers. He
could think of no argument. He would like his son to
be up again and well. But how could the doctor make
another leg? Finally, with a pessimistic gesture he
turned the boy over to William who amputated the
infected leg. "Just how are you going to give him a
new leg?" It was Mary who asked the important
question. William's answer was brief. "Watch
me." She had watched as he went to a bamboo clump,
cut down a tree, then with patience and ingenuity
fashioned a workable pair of crutches for the young
man to use when he recovered. "Now you can walk
again," he informed the delighted youth several
weeks later. The young man salaamed his gratitude
until William thought he would break in the middle.
Shortly after that the aged father creaked into the
dispensary in his dilapidated ox cart and fell at the
doctor's feet. "Sahib," he cried, "you are my
Guru. You have my everlasting gratitude. May God
give you long life and prosperity." And with an
eloquent gesture he presented William with a cack-

ling hen and a bundle of small idols, saying, " Sahib, take these, I am not praying to idols any more."

William was dictating again. " Eyes and cataracts, one thousand and sixty-four."

" Eyes and cataracts, one thousand sixty-four." Mary wrote swiftly and accurately, but her mind was occupied with the meaning back of these figures. She could never keep the tears from her eyes when one who was blind was given sight. Mary knew that the ordinary scenes about her would never become dull for she was always seeing them with the fresh, released vision of the recovered blind.

" Tumor operations," said William with pride, " ninety-five." Next to removing cataracts and giving sight, there was no operation which afforded William greater satisfaction than ridding the native people of the burden of tumor. He paused in his dictation and smiled. He was in his operating room again, the close, sweet odor of chloroform hovered in the air, his instruments gleamed bright and clean. On the table lay a middle-aged man, a native farmer, afflicted with the most distressing growth William had yet witnessed. This man, whose livelihood depended upon the soil, daily dragged a terrible thirty-five pound weight through the intricacies of farming. The continual pain had left marks of deepest suffering about the mouth and in the squinting, brown eyes. And now he was to be relieved.

William uttered a sigh of satisfaction. There was

no doubt but that his crisp, brown beard had inspired
more confidence in his ability.   He recalled with
pleasure that he had not been called " young fellow "
since the beard was heavy enough to cover his face.
His youthfulness was no longer a drawback but an
advantage, for it enabled him to do the work of two
men while his beard gave him the dignity of a man of
fifty.   The young doctor felt justified in his moment
of pride.

" Ulcers, twenty-six; bones, fifty-six; ear, nose and
throat, twenty-nine . . ."   William's voice crisply
recited the year's work as Mary took down the figures.
As they finished, Mary gazed with pride upon the
total.   One thousand, seven hundred and ninety-three
operations in one year.   This was in addition to the
three hundred and forty-four medical cases and the
five thousand who came only for medicines which she
had previously recorded.   No wonder the people loved
the doctor.   No wonder he was approached with more
deference than many of their gods.

The little dispensary had long been overcrowded,
and the name of William Wanless took on something
of the ring of magic.   Many a native traveler was
making a new kind of pilgrimage.   Instead of going
to a temple of the ancient gods, the destination was
the temple of the White Wizard.   High castes and
outcastes jammed the courtyard and dispensary.

" We're just going to have to have more room,"

Mary complained as she climbed into the small tonga with her mysterious husband.

She had accused him of being mysterious at the dinner table when he suggested that they spend their Sunday afternoon driving to Miraj, five miles east of Sangli. They had taken one of these mystifying drives two Sundays before. Mary had been puzzled. After traveling the five miles to the outskirts of the well-populated village, William had stopped the tonga before a large space of dry, rocky land and had just sat and looked. And he steadfastly refused to answer her questions as to why they were there. Instead he sat with a provocative smile while his eyes filled with visions.

" You're just teasing me," Mary had accused, slapping his arm. In answer he had drawn her close, saying nothing.

Now they were making the trip again. This time she wouldn't give him the satisfaction of questions, she decided, and as the tonga lurched along the road Mary confined her conversation to the work of the dispensary.

As she had anticipated, they once again drew up before the large, rocky plot of ground. " You can stop here," William directed the tonga-walla, Shanker. Mary bit her lip. What was in William's mind? He glanced at her mischievously from the corner of his eye.

" Miraj is a central place," he observed.

" Yes, isn't it ? " She was sweetly agreeable, vowing not to ask one single question.

" The railroad comes through here, too. This is on the main line from Bombay to Bangalore, and . . ." he added brightly, " there's a branch line to Kolhapur and one to Sholapur."

" I know." She nodded pleasantly.

" And roads from scores of villages." He was looking at her now, in a moment he was going to say something important. And then Mary gasped. Her pose was dropped in a burst of enthusiasm.

" William! Are you thinking of —— ? "

Before she could finish her question he broke in. " A hospital! " He grasped her hands, his face filled with enthusiasm. " It's a perfect location. Easy to get to, not far from the railroad station, and close enough to the village to be of use, but not too close for contamination." His voice shook with excitement. " Mary, there are twelve acres here. Imagine what we could build on them." He leaned forward, one arm about her shoulders as he visualized the picture. " A first-class hospital with a real operating theatre, great airy wards, a building just for children. Why, there's room to expand and build for years and years."

" Oh! " He had caught her up in the vision. Buildings rose like magic from the wasteland. "A hospital with all modern conveniences! And with the operating theatre we can have a real sterilizer and maybe enough hot water when we need it! "

" By all means! "

" And a laboratory? "

" And a laboratory."

Mary caught her breath. " William, it's wonderful," she whispered.

He kissed her cheek. " We'll make something real
for India here," prophesied William, his voice full of
dreams.

As suddenly as she had caught her enthusiasm, it
faded from her voice. A distressing thought occurred
to Mary. " Where will you get the money? " The
visualized buildings seemed to melt into the earth.

William looked at his wife searchingly, then made
the comment that always piqued her but later made
her sigh with wonder. " The Lord will provide," he
assured his helpmate and squeezed her hand cozily.

Dubious grey eyes turned upon him. " How much
land do you think you—er—He will provide? "

" Twelve acres." The answer was given without
hesitation. Evidently William had been thinking
about this for some time. " From there," he pointed
to a distant jutting rock, " to there." And his gesture included a group of miserable, filthy huts belonging to a group of untouchables.

" But what about those people? You can't just
order them off their land."

" There's always a way to deal constructively with
every problem, my dear." Then with an eager look,
" I've written to the Bryn Mawr church telling them

of our need. I mentioned that ten thousand dollars would give us a nice start."

Ten thousand dollars! The figure staggered Mary. But William spoke of the amount as if it had been ten cents. "He'll get his hospital," she thought and looked at his eager, purposeful face with unashamed admiration.

As the tonga jounced back along the road to Sangli William cocked his head to one side and permitted himself the rare pleasure of retrogression. "Mary," he cuddled her hand in his, "do you remember that Goddess Kali we saw in Bombay?"

Mary shuddered even at the memory. "Will I ever forget?"

His voice was strangely ashamed. "I didn't tell you at the time, Mary, but she gave me quite a jolt. Somehow," he settled back in the tonga, "somehow she seemed to be personally antagonistic toward me. It was all imagination, of course. But I had the feeling that she, or what she represented, was going to make it hard for me. But you know when I think of our new hospital, even of the work we've done so far, that Goddess seems a long, long way off. I don't want to brag, but I have a feeling that we're making headway." It was evident William was happy and pleased. So was Mary. With her gloved finger tips she caressed her husband's gentle hands while she looked up into his beaming face.

"Hello, there! What's going on up ahead?"

William stiffened to attention. Mary followed his glance.

On the road before them walked a group of weary travelers. As the tonga drew near a woman lurched, flung up her arms and with a shrill cry fell to the ground.

" Shanker, stop! "

William jumped out and went to the woman's side. Her traveling companions turned and bolted down the road toward Sangli.

Mary gazed after the fleeing natives angrily. " A lot of good Samaritans they are," she said indignantly.

William's attention was riveted on the sick woman. Great, dark blotches showed under her skin. William's lips tightened. Immediately he felt the gland in her armpit. Swollen. As he examined her, heavy dark blood issued from the nostrils. Mary started to alight from the tonga. " Stay where you are," he ordered sharply.

" But what is it? " queried Mary, wondering at William's suddenly grave face. " Shouldn't we take her back to the dispensary with us? Wouldn't that be the best thing to do? "

" No," the answer was curt. " There's morphine in my medicine case. Fix a hypodermic." Then he changed his mind. " I'll take care of it myself," he said, taking the medicine case. " Now, listen, and do as I say. This is urgent. You get back to Sangli before those travelers reach the village. Tell Mr.

"William jumped out and went to the woman's side."

Greyson to *keep these strangers out of the village!*
They're not to come near. And don't touch them
whatever you do!" He drew a sharp breath. " Is
that clear?"

"Yes," answered the surprised Mary. " But I
don't know why ——"

William's voice was grim, and his words like a sen-
tence of death. " This is plague, Mary. Plague."

Terror showed in her eyes.

"Now do as I say," he directed. " Hurry!
Hurry!"

As the tonga-walla hurried Mary back to Sangli,
William again turned to the sick woman.

She twinged feebly when the hypodermic needle
plunged into her blotched flesh and for an instant
great, dark eyes gazed gratefully into William's.
The morphine cast a warm, comforting blanket about
her pain.

" She has only a few minutes," the doctor observed
to himself. He must make sure that the body would
be disposed of quickly, that the spreading of the
disease might be checked if possible. " Thank
heaven," breathed William, " for my medical journals." He thought with gratitude of a recent
article carrying the story of the discovery of bacillus
pestis, the plague germ. Controversy raged in medical circles as to the truth of the findings made by
Kitasato and Yersin at Hong Kong within recent
months, but William relied upon these findings.
Knowing India was a plague country, the doctor

found it difficult to suppress his impatience at the meager knowledge of science regarding this deadly disease. One medical journal had mentioned that the plague, or black death, was known as far back as the first century B.C. and first appeared in Constantinople in 543 A.D. From that time it had raged at intermittent periods taking a huge toll of life.

The doctor wiped the perspiration from his forehead, looked at the woman. She was dying. With a disease as ancient as the decaying temples of Hinduism, this woman of the nineteenth century was dying. William shook his head. Here was a challenge—a challenge rising from the dust of ages.

Suddenly, with a tired, dry gasp, the woman died.

The clumping of a horse's hooves and a loud voice issued from clouds of dust coming down the road.

" Doctor-sahib! "

It was Shanker returning on horseback to fetch William. Gratefully the doctor mounted the horse, the excited boy running along beside him.

" Doctor-sahib," he gasped out as the horse headed toward Sangli, " these travelers, I have talked with them. They come from Poona and already the plague is there. From Bombay the people came bringing it with them. And now they come here." He was trembling with fear. " Let us leave this place, quickly! I do not want to die," he shivered.

" That's exactly why the disease spreads," he told the frightened boy. " People carry it from one place to another. The thing to do is stay where you are and fumigate, segregate and inoculate!" He spurred the horse into a trot, pleased with the words. They would make a good slogan. "Fumigate, segregate and inoculate!"

But fear had already gripped the Sangli villagers. Even now, on the outskirts of town a straggling procession formed, headed away from the dreaded plague carriers. They had packed hurriedly, fearfully. In addition to a baby or child on her hip, each woman carried a basket of rice and condiments on her head, while the men carried cooking pots and blankets in a bag slung over their backs. These constituted the belongings which would accompany the troubled travelers in their escape.

Drawing the horse to a quick stop William recognized many of the dark faces before him.

"Wait," he commanded. "Where are you going?" To his surprise they cast only quick, furtive glances at him and continued on their way. William saw a man whose eyesight he had restored.

"You," he called. "Where are you going?" The man glanced at William, shook his head and plodded on.

"Wait, all of you!" William pleaded in vain, they walked past him, faces stolid, eyes frightened.

"You cannot escape the plague by running away from it," he called. "You must stay at home and fight it. Don't spread this disease all over India. Take the responsibility of stopping it in your own village!" But his words fell on unheeding ears.

The sound of an approaching tonga clattered above the soft shuffle of travelers' feet. As the dust cleared, William was treated to the sight of Mary in a tonga driven by Victoria May. The older woman sat grim and iron-jawed as she brought the horse to a standstill. Mary jumped out and ran toward William.

"We couldn't do anything with them," she cried, referring to the earlier travelers whom she was to have kept apart from the villagers. "The minute they came into town everybody rushed to meet them. They told all about the plague and the sick woman on the road and how everybody's dying in Bombay and Poona and all along the coast!"

Victoria May approached with a white face. When she spoke her voice was like ice. "There was a dead rat outside the schoolroom this morning."

"You burned it?"

"Yes." Her voice grew low. "Cecelia Greyson complained of headache a few minutes ago."

William looked again at the line of departing villagers but their stolid faces told him that nothing he could say would stop their flight from plague. He called out to Mary and Victoria May, "We'll go to the mission compound." And headed his horse in that direction.

In her small bungalow Mrs. Greyson was battling between anxiety for her daughter, and a desire to appear courteous to a most illustrious guest.

Not ten minutes before a carriage had swung into

the compound and a neatly-dressed servant had inquired for Dr. William Wanless.

Sensing the importance of the visitor in the carriage, Mrs. Greyson had offered him an invitation to come inside and await the doctor's return. Her invitation was accepted, and the humble Greyson dwelling was graced by the highly decorative presence of the Prime Minister of Miraj, the Honorable Krishnaji Chandra.

For ten lengthy minutes Mrs. Greyson had done everything within her power to make pleasant conversation, but the stout little man would only talk in monosyllables, if at all. " I can't tell if he's snubbing me or is just preoccupied," the motherly woman thought, then hearing Cecelia's troubled fretting felt a most unmotherly desire to shove this pompous man out onto the verandah and tend to her sick daughter.

The clattering of horses' hooves announced William's return.

" Here he is at last! " cried Mrs. Greyson. " I'll bring him right in here, Mr. Chandra." She scurried from the room, soon returning with William, who carried a look of surprise on his face.

After the proper introductions and felicitations, the Prime Minister came straight to the point.

' I am here at the command of His Highness, the Rajah of Miraj. He has heard of your work as a doctor and has been impressed." He cleared his throat. William nodded and eagerly awaited the next words.

" Once again the dreaded plague is sweeping over our beloved country. Some rats, carriers of the disease, have been found dead and there are already two cases in town." The dark brows were raised. " His Highness the Rajah is greatly distressed as you can well imagine." William again nodded.

" In his agitation and distress he has sent me to you."

" I understand." William's curiosity prickled. What did this man want?

" In the past," he studied the tips of his thin brown fingers, " we found nothing effective to combat the epidemic. We have heard what splendid work you are doing, and so we turn to you." There was an elaborate bow of the head followed by a deep breath. " His Highness graciously implores you to accept the post of Sanitary Inspector and Medical Officer for his State." The voice paused. " May I inform him that you will accept? "

William let the Greyson clock tick uninterrupted for several seconds. The Rajah of Miraj! Sanitary Inspector and Medical Officer! A chance to work with the Indian people—at the request of their Rajah. Then he remembered the natives' lack of response in matters of sanitation. Their reluctance and hesitation in accepting new ideas. What good would it do to issue orders if people refused to obey? William stroked his beard as he considered his lack of experience in treating this disease called " black death." He hesitated as he thought of the revolu-

tionary moves he would have to insist upon—and
would the people accept them?

Krishnaji Chandra seemed to understand the doctor's hesitation. He smiled silkily. " You will be
given a free hand. The Rajah has asked me to say
that the life or death of the inhabitants of Miraj will
be in your hands."

In his hands. William glanced down at his hands.
He was stirred as a sense of power coursed through
them. These hands had performed difficult operations, painlessly and carefully dressed gaping
wounds. Yes, they could accept the present challenge, too! Fumigate, segregate, inoculate. That
was the answer. In this way hundreds would be
saved and he had the Prime Minister's promise that
every order would be enforced.

William smiled. " You will extend my thanks to
His Highness," he directed, " and tell him I accept
with pleasure the great honor conferred upon me."

To William's surprise no look of gratitude flashed
over the face of the state official. Rather, his face
became mask-like as he salaamed gracefully, then departed in the shining state carriage as silently as he
had come.

" Well," the doctor tapped his fingers reflectively,
" I don't believe the Prime Minister is very happy
about my acceptance." But he cast the idea from his
mind and turned to a consideration of the immediate
problem. This great, new challenge filled William
with eager anticipation. A chance to pit his strength

and medical knowledge against one of India's darkest terrors.

Mrs. Greyson touched his sleeve. " Dr. Wanless," she said trying to keep the anxiety from her voice, " Cecelia has a pesky headache. I wonder if you'd mind looking at her? "

" Not at all," he said in a suddenly serious voice, and followed Mrs. Greyson into the bedroom.

Cecelia, having gratefully shed awkward adolescence, had emerged a lively and attractive young lady. But today she didn't care whether she looked attractive or not. Her head ached unbearably.

" I don't feel well," she complained. " In fact, I feel terrible."

The hotness in her face brought out a few errant freckles. William put his gentle hand to her forehead. There was a high fever. Mrs. Greyson twisted her handkerchief, bit her lower lip. She knew that the plague had come to Sangli.

" Put out your tongue," William said to Cecelia. She obeyed. William stared. He crossed his knee, stroked his beard thoughtfully. When he spoke his voice was grim.

" Young lady . . ."

" Yes? " quivered Cecelia. Mrs. Greyson hardly dared to breathe.

" What have you been eating? " The question came as a complete surprise. Cecelia's eyes popped wide open. The doctor stared back at her. Slowly the girl lowered fringed eyelids. A crimson blush, born of embarrassment, spread over her face. Dropping her voice she murmured hesitantly:

"Mama received a box of bon bons and chocolates from America, and I ate them all up."

Mrs. Greyson's eyes dilated. "What?!"

Cecelia raised calf-like eyes. "And all at one time." Then an afterthought. "This morning."

William could have shouted with sheer relief.

"Young lady," he boomed, "it's castor oil for you!" And with a hearty handshake he informed the relieved Mrs. Greyson, "She's bilious. Thank the Lord, she's only bilious!"

6

THE DREAD black plague struck in all its fury. Breaking out in Hong Kong it gathered momentum and rolled like a tidal wave over Asia, into Calcutta, across central India, then crashed down the west coast claiming thousands. The earth groaned with the dead and dying and fear hung over every heart. And down from the cities, like frantic ants searching, searching for a place of safety, scurried the terrified natives, fleeing from death. Into the villages they thronged while in their belongings, on their bodies and in their hair they carried the messenger of death, the horrible rat-flea.

Western India roads were clogged with agonized victims fallen sick by the way. Abandoned by hysterical relatives, children wept over the dead bodies of parents, themselves doomed to perish from plague or starvation. Helpless fear drove the fugitives relentlessly as they fought to escape the deadly menace which they could not understand.

Slackening up his work at the Sangli dispensary, William plunged into the task of Sanitary Inspector for Miraj with a simple, direct approach. Although handicapped by science's meager knowledge of the disease he dared use his common sense and the authority given him by the Rajah.

" Cleanliness is imperative for health," he an-

nounced to the Prime Minister and immediately
started out on his bicycle to inspect the residence section of town.

He had known what to expect. Natives of Miraj
were no different from natives of Sangli. There were
the cheerless, small mud houses, the tile roofs, the
front yards with the ever-present cow, sheep or goat.

" Clean up your yards," William directed. " Keep
your animals behind the house—and *out* of the
house! "

He was met with a storm of protest. " The Doctor-
sahib asks the impossible! " " Animals are *always*
kept in the front yard. It's more convenient! "
" Why should we clean up our yards? We've always
lived this way."

House to house, hour after hour, William patiently
explained the situation. The plague was moving in.
Miraj must be safeguarded. Cleanliness will help
to save the children. But they must hurry. Those
animals must be put in the field or in the back yard.
The front yard must be cleaned immediately . . . and
hiding the dirt under leaves did not mean cleanliness.

Explicitly-directed street cleaners were told to
circulate through the village, but many loitered about,
gossiping and paying no heed to the instructions
given them. William lectured to some hastily-ap-
pointed helpers, earnestly requesting their cooperation in cleaning up the homes, but few responded with
constructive action. The doctor himself tirelessly
inspected, suggested and plead with the dwellers of

Miraj—but years of ignorance and distrust of foreigners loomed like a foreboding curtain to his efforts at sanitation.

" Yes, yes." Heads nodded understandingly as he pointed out the dangers of flies on their food and the vermin in their houses.

" Yes, yes." Mothers' voices chimed approval as he instructed in the simple rules of hygiene. But as soon as the Doctor-sahib disappeared down the street on his bicycle, his advice was forgotten. Why not keep the animals in the house? It saved footsteps. Why take trouble to put garments upon the babies?

Babai, an ancient, matted-haired, shriveled old medicine man, warned the villagers: " Beware of the White Doctor. He brings bad idea. You will displease your gods by listening to him. Come to me. I will drive away the evil spirits of plague." With trust in their hearts the villagers listened to Babai. There had always been a Babai to drive away the evil spirits. The shriveled old man chanted prayers, offered cocoanut oil and rice to their deities, and seared the stomachs of screaming infants with his hot iron brand. " I will drive away the evil spirits of plague," chanted Babai, and the villagers clung to him, hopefully. Meanwhile cow dung lay in their front yards, and babies crawled in filth. Goats wandered at will and vermin scurried here and there.

Suddenly, a man fell in the street—dead. Several children became ill, their heads ached, their stomachs hurt, and then the dreaded swelling of the glands in

armpit, neck and groin. Plague had come to Miraj
and was catching like a brush fire.

" We'll inoculate everyone now! " ordered William. With his life-saving hypodermic needle and
the precious serum just arrived from Bombay, he
went to the homes. But the doors were locked.

" You must be inoculated," William called out.
" It will save your lives! "

But the terrified natives crouched in their dark
hovels and covered their ears. Hadn't their own
medicine man, Babai, told them of this deadly stuff in
a needle? It would not only be useless for plague, but
would eventually result in the most dreaded disease—
leprosy. So while his aides blustered and threatened
and William pleaded, the natives refused the serum
and clung to the ways of Babai.

William approached the Prime Minister.

" We must have a segregation ward," he said.
" In that way we can isolate the contagious cases."
His voice sounded a warning. " And we had better
build it now."

William expected to obtain the Prime Minister's
immediate consent, and was greatly surprised when
the smiling official answered.

" Perhaps," he parried, stroking his ear lobe
thoughtfully, " we had better wait for awhile."

" Wait? " the doctor replied. " The plague is
here! People are dying! "

The hesitant Krishnaji Chandra tapped his foot
reflectively. William was puzzled at this reluctance.

" I've tried to inoculate the people. They refuse. The next best thing is a segregation ward."

In answer the stout official pursed his lips. A suspicion crossed the doctor's mind.

" Mr. Chandra, do you by any chance doubt the value of modern medicine? " There was a pause. The official's face became mask-like. William continued. " You, yourself, have permitted me to inoculate you. Have you any doubts as to the efficiency of the vaccine for others? "

At last the pompous one spoke. " The gods are unpredictable," he murmured. " I have spent much time and money appeasing *my* gods. But those others . . ." He left the statement in mid-air.

William gasped. " It isn't possible," he thought. " It isn't possible for an educated, otherwise intelligent man to hold such beliefs."

Smiling quietly, the Prime Minister spoke. " We, in India, do not move in a hurry. There is a lot of time."

" I realize that fully," William answered, shaken. " But I was appointed Sanitary Inspector—and with full powers—by your Rajah! And as Sanitary Inspector I demand a segregation ward or I will not be responsible for the health of your people! "

A tremendous calm settled down upon the Hindu and he seemed to sink back into the lap of Himalayan eternity. A superior smile played upon his lips. " Emotion, my friend, is unbecoming a state official. Even a Sanitary Inspector."

Clenching his teeth, the doctor nodded, then strode from the room.

Another day passed. More dead. William had to hire the most despised of all outcasts, scavengers, to remove the bodies. Other native helpers had succumbed to terror. The death cart rattled its gruesome way through the streets, picking up and spewing its grim cargo outside the village where the bodies were cremated. All this William had to supervise, and still the villagers clung to the ways of Babai.

It was an early afternoon when an excited, breathless Mary found her husband supervising the fumigation of houses.

" That medicine man," Mary cried. " That Babai! Oh, William, come quickly! "

The doctor stared at his wife. Tears ran down her face. " What's the matter? " he asked anxiously.

She pointed up the street. " A little girl is sick and that fiend, that—that beast is beating her! " William had never seen his wife so upset.

" Beating her? "

She quivered. " I can't get her screams out of my ears. You must do something about it—right now! "

He patted her shoulder, then hurried into the street. A crowd was gathered about a miserable hut in the distance. William sighed. The medicine man had been trying to drive out evil spirits with a big stick.

As William approached the dwelling he was surprised at the unspoken greeting in several faces.

Before they had been afraid of the doctor's needle. Why didn't they scowl now? And then he discovered the reason.

Inside the hut, a sad little heap on the floor was the mortal remains of the tiny girl sufferer. Dying of plague, she had lived but a few moments after Babai's torturous beating. The still little body was twisted in agony and the marks of Babai's devil-beating oozed blood over her cold flesh.

William felt his heart grow faint. With preventative inoculation she could have been saved.

" Doctor-sahib." The voice belonged to the dead child's father. William turned.

" Yes? "

The trembling Hindu, his arms about his small son, pushed the boy toward the doctor.

" You use needle for son. You fix." The voice was faint, but there was faith in his eyes.

William gathered the small boy to him. Then a neighbor with her child, and then a young woman stepped to the doctor's side.

" You fix us."

" You give us needle. We not afraid."

William looked into their faces. The ancient prejudices were breaking down. These people were asking for a better way. If only they could all embrace the new ways—the better ways.

Next day there were more deaths in the village.

" Oh, dear," worried Mary. " If they'd only take your word for it. All these lives could be saved."

William's heart was heavy. " I wish they would," he said fervently. " But—it seems that we only learn through suffering. If there was just an easier way to tear down old ideas . . . " His mind was troubled. The dead had been cremated this morning. Tomorrow morning there would be more.

Babai, furious and frustrated by the mounting deaths, spewed threats upon questioning natives, terrorized them with the wrath of the gods and called down curses upon the heads of those who forsook the old way for the new.

" Go home and pray to your gods," he shrieked to onlookers as he beat a sick woman, trying to rid her of unclean spirits.

" Out! . . . Out! " His matted hair tossed about as he howled at the spirits and brought the stiff wood down upon the woman's tortured body. " Out! Out! "

The people were afraid to remonstrate.

Again William went to the Prime Minister. " Babai's patients are dying every day. Those I have inoculated are untouched. Isn't that proof that the new ways are best? "

The Prime Minister nodded.

" We must have that segregation building! " The doctor emphasized his words by beating his fist upon the desk.

" The building will be erected soon," negligently replied the official and would give William no further satisfaction.

William's improvised headquarters thronged with people begging for inoculation. Babai, barbed by darts of jealousy, renewed his threats upon his now doubting followers and fought savagely to maintain his position of esteem. But the people had seen a new way, a way that was proving itself superior. Gradually they deserted Babai and his ancient cures; turned to the new doctor. But the knowledge came too late for many doubters. There were more and more victims of the black death.

One morning William was given the heartening news that the segregation building had been started. Within two days the corrugated-iron structure was up and he was moving patients into it. But the morning death cart picked up its ever-increasing number of dead. Like a gluttonous vulture, gorged and heavy with its odious meal, the crude conveyance rumbled and groaned through the chilled streets drawn by flabby bullocks insensible to their gruesome cargo. Quicklime in mammoth pits was necessary to consume the large number of villagers who, except for ignorance and superstition, might still have lived.

A few days later, while making his regular tour of inspection, William found a tightly closed house. Breaking the lock and entering he found seven plague dead—and one live baby. The family had listened to Babai—and had perished.

It became vividly apparent that nothing short of the most stringent methods would help these people. They could be trusted to do nothing for themselves.

Much as he disliked dealing with the Prime Minister, William made another call.

" I want to discuss the problem of rats," William began.

" That, Dr. Wanless, is easy to discuss—very difficult to solve."

The doctor nodded. " I understand. But if the rats are not destroyed we cannot destroy the plague. In ordinary times it's bad enough. Rats eat food in the houses, they live among you like pets, and they also eat your stored grain. But now—if they are not killed it means death for hundreds of your people."

Krishnaji Chandra shrugged his plump shoulders. " Your ways are opposed to our religion. A Hindu will not take life."

" But to save himself and his family," argued William, " he should be at least willing to kill a few rats."

There was no reply.

An idea came to William. " Suppose," he began, " we should offer a reward for every rat killed. Would that break down the prejudice? Would not these poor people be glad to get the money? "

The official shook his head. " No."

" But don't *you* realize the importance of killing the rats? " He felt exasperated at this lack of concern about life and death.

" When a man dies it is the will of the gods," the Prime Minister explained with a lazy gesture.

William jumped to his feet. " I was asked to take

the post of Sanitary Inspector. I intend to rid Miraj
of rats if I have to do it with my own two hands!"

"Excellent." The other's smile was mocking.

"As Sanitary Inspector appointed by your Rajah,
I order all houses to be vacated at once and the population moved to the hills!"

Krishnaji Chandra raised dubious eyes. "Suppose the villagers refuse to go?"

"You will order them to go—in the name of their
Rajah!"

There was no comment. The Prime Minister rose,
accompanied his visitor to the door. When he finally
spoke his words held little hope. "I'll do what I
can," he said, but his expressive shoulders shrugged
pessimistically.

After two more urgent visits from William the
Prime Minister reluctantly ordered the village vacated. All inhabitants were ordered to go to the
nearby hills and camp until their dwellings had been
officially fumigated, the tile roofs removed to let the
fierce tropical sun deal with lurking germs, and the
death-carrying rats killed.

The wails and lamentations were terrible to hear.

"We're being driven out like cattle," howled some
of the women. "Turned out of our own houses,"
growled furious men, their black eyes snapping in the
bright sunlight. "They mean to take our homes,"
prophesied a palsied old woman. And all the while
they forgot that except for official decree they would

have fled the village terrified at the first sign of plague.

There were those who stubbornly resisted the white doctor; others who had submitted to inoculation were angry at the thought of leaving their homes, while some gladly obeyed, sensing the wonder-working ability of this young man from a far-off place called Canada.

Thus began the exodus to the hills. Gradually the thin, unwilling file of villagers massed in swarms upon the hillsides, dotting the barren land with dried-grass huts and crude shelters of sorts. Those who were well remained in the clean outdoors, but the segregation building choked with its contaminated burden. And all the while the gruesome disinfection and disposal of the dead continued day after day after day.

To William the plague nightmare seemed unending.

The forms of the living and the lifeless grew to look alike. The horrible, rot-colored blotches caused by undertaken hemorrhages, the choking of the dying, the wailing of the bereaved—these were with William hourly.

The odor of disinfectant hung about him like a nightmarish fog and filled his nostrils every moment. Life took on a seemingly never-ending pattern fashioned by a bloodsucking monster from the depths. Up early with the dying, new faces to take their places on the improvised cots and beds and on the floors; the everlasting disinfecting of the village homes, the cleaning up and scrubbing and valiant attempts to make the place inhabitable, and the squeaking, squealing, scurrying rats in traps, dying of poison or burning in furry funeral pyres. William worked automatically now. Sometimes he slept . . . sometimes he didn't. A bitter, rancid odor hung heavy over the hills and village of Miraj. On, on, on came the procession of corpses.

And then, one morning, there were no dead.

William raised his haggard eyes to the sunlight. How good it felt! How good to face the early morning in company with the living. William's weariness dropped from him like a cape. He breathed deeply, fully, of the fresh clean air. How bright was the countryside. How brilliant the colors. What a relief that the days of horror were past.

Now there was no need for anyone to stay longer in the hills.

With happy steps, homeward bound, the villagers of Miraj returned to their houses to find them clean, pure and free from contamination. There were those who thanked him, but William's greatest thanks came from the knowledge that with his own two hands he had helped break through their bonds of ignorance and superstition. With his own two hands.

As he sank down into a deep, much-needed sleep he thought of the Blood Goddess Kali, but her power seemed weak, and his strong. He was serving to his utmost.

7

MARY FELT wholeheartedly grateful to the Prime Minister for his visit. The day had gone by like a hurried dream. She came wearily to the door of the dispensary for a breath of fresh air. The voices of Krishnaji Chandra and William floated out over the warm, heavy atmosphere. It was good to be away from the sweetish bland odor of chloroform; away from the patient suffering of the sick natives even for a moment. Already there had been several operations that afternoon. Mary sank into a chair on the mud verandah, closed her eyes, and tried to forget the white masks, sterilized instruments, the spurting blood.

She let her mind dwell on the purpose of the Prime Minister's visit. She kept on wondering if a magnificent gift was to be offered.

"Do you think the Rajah of Miraj will show his gratitude for your work during the plague?" Yesterday she had asked William and he had smiled at her eager question.

"Wouldn't be surprised," he'd answered and they had grinned together wondering what form this gratitude would take.

"He might present us with an elephant." The suggestion had been Mary's.

But William's mind was more practical. "I'd

much rather have a good operating table or some new equipment."

" It might be money."

He shook his head, closed one eye thoughtfully. " I don't think so. But," here he had yawned deeply, " whatever it is, I'm glad for one thing: that the plague is over! "

" If I were a deacon, I'd say ' amen ' to that! " And they'd both laughed and gone on wondering.

And now, today, she was still wondering. " If I listen more carefully," thought Mary, " I may be able to hear what they're saying." But it required such an effort and she was too tired. Suddenly her errant attention was focused upon a commotion across the street.

" It is true! "

" Come hear what has happened! "

" Good luck has come to us! "

A crowd was rapidly gathering at the stall of the pottery maker. This smiling, quiet native had been overworked these last few days, for it was the time of Naga-Panchami, the snake festival, when India attempts to appease the wrathful cobra. " More than twenty thousand die every year from snake-bite," William had told her. Mary could see the half-naked potter, his dripping hands covered with wet clay, feverishly fashioning miniature cobras. As she had walked down the village street that morning Mary had noticed that every hut displayed images of the snake and those people too poor to buy a model from

the potter created their own from mud. In court-
yards, on verandahs, in the houses and on the streets,
mud and clay snakes received the homage of Sangli
villagers. Some tiny images were nearly obscured by
red paste, white paste, garlands of zinnias and jasmine. Small clay saucers filled with milk could be
seen everywhere. " If a cobra drinks milk from their
saucer," Victoria May had explained, " they have
the idea that good luck will follow all year."

" We have luck! "

" Good fortune! Good fortune! "

The excited voices at the potter's stall issued from
a family of ten whose humble dwelling had been
honored by a visit from an obliging cobra which
drank every drop of milk from the proffered clay
saucer.

" It was not five minutes ago . . ." The voluble,
lank father recited over and over again the story of
their good luck to a fast-growing crowd of curious villagers. The wife, no less talkative but her voice
lowered in deference to her husband, circulated on the
outskirts of the multiplying crowd repeating and repeating the story until in the short space of ten minutes the original facts had been so delightfully em-
bellished that the tale would serve as a family legend
for generations. Tiny sons and daughters, conscious
of their increased importance in the community,
strutted before envious friends.

Mary wondered at the Indian's childish appease-
ment of the cobra; at the dread hooded serpent itself

with its sinuous movements and quick attack. She
must have dozed, for she was awakened by the close-
ness of voices. The Prime Minister was leaving.
Mary's drowsiness disappeared, driven out by curiosity. How would the Rajah of Miraj show his
gratitude? What had William learned? The Prime
Minister's loose-flowing, brocaded clothing made a
sudden splash of color against the white building as
he appeared in the doorway. The gold threads in his
turban glittered as he salaamed to Mary, bade good
day to the doctor, and was gone.

Mary tried to wait until the plump official was out
of earshot, then she grasped William's arm eagerly.
"What did he say?" A pinprick of anxiety deflated
her eagerness. William didn't look excited—only
thoughtful. "William!"

He sensed his wife's thoughts and patted her hand.
He was wondering just how to tell her.

"But what did he say?" she insisted. If they
hadn't been grateful, if they didn't appreciate all he
had done . . .

William walked to the edge of the mud verandah,
his hands in his pockets. She itched to pursue the
question, but she knew from experience that William
was going to tell her. It was just a matter of time.
Checking her impatience, Mary went to her husband,
patted his shoulder, flecked imaginary specks from
his white suit.

"Hmmm." There, now he was about to speak.
"Yes, William?" she answered brightly.

" The Rajah of Miraj is grateful for our work during the plague."

" Yes? " She held her breath.

" And," he paced down the length of the verandah, his brows drawn together, " he wants to express his gratitude in the most satisfactory manner."

" William! " Mary stamped her foot impatiently and said with a little laugh: " Is it an elephant or a new operating table? "

" Neither."

" Well? "

Ordinarily William would have been amused at his wife's pins-and-needles excitement, but now he only sank into a chair and pulled at his beard. Indian officials had a way of being subtle which often puzzled the frank, outspoken Canadian doctor. William thought of the Prime Minister's words. " The Rajah wishes me to convey his gratitude to you and offers to grant any favor you may ask." There was no offer of money, equipment, or anything tangible, but instead the offer of a favor to be granted. William tapped his lip with his finger. He suddenly felt like a man who's been granted a wish and didn't know which of his desires he dared gratify. A favor. Could he ask for a hospital? But that might be considered presumptuous. And if he asked for a new operating table or a piece of equipment would that appear too small a desire to be worthy of the State of Miraj? If only these people would be more explicit. Could they not change their ways for modern ones?

William yearned for the straightforward business methods of his Canadian friends.

" William Wanless! " Mary planted herself before him, an irate little figure whose curiosity could no longer be denied.

William looked at her, jumped up from his chair. " Mary, he's offered to grant any favor we may ask."

" A favor? " The unexpectedness of the offer surprised her.

" A favor," he repeated.

" Oh." As she turned aside her exclamation was river-bottom deep. A favor sounded so weak, so vague beside her vivid images of an elephant or other Indian magnificence. The reality was shuffled about in her mind and before a minute had passed Mary quickly squeezed optimism out of it. " *Any* favor did he say? " Plans and ideas formed changing patterns in her eyes.

" Well, yes." There was a trace of hesitation in William's voice.

" But if he said *any* favor," Mary began enthusiastically but William stopped her with a word.

" Wait."

She looked at her husband curiously. Wait? She could think of a dozen favors to ask.

But William was pacing the verandah again, his hands deep in his pockets. " During the plague the Prime Minister gave me a good piece of advice. I think it wise to remember. He said, ' We in India do not move in a hurry. There is plenty of time.'

Plenty of time," he repeated thoughtfully and decided to wait. Someday he would want a favor granted—and then he would ask.

Mary glanced quickly at him, her eyes dimming with rapidly-dying plans.

" But ——" she stopped. There was a time when she would have argued, made suggestions and exchanged ideas. Now—she raised her eyebrows murmuring, " Yes, William," and turned into the dispensary. A terrible question arose in her breast. " Am I becoming just a missionary's wife?" The thought gripped her. " Perhaps I'm getting old." But suddenly she didn't care. Why argue with William? His judgment always proved better than hers anyway. She set about automatically to clean up the operating room and sterilize the instruments for tomorrow's use.

" Doctor-sahib! Doctor-sahib!" An excited voice which sounded like Rama, the leper boy, broke through William's thoughts. It *was* Rama. As the faithful boy dashed into the courtyard and toward the dispensary verandah William felt a glow of happiness. Although Rama's disease was not cured, it had been checked and with proper precautions he was able to circulate among his friends. William shuddered as he visualized Rama's probable condition had he and Mary left Sangli and visited the Taj Mahal.

Rama held a letter in his shaking hand. " Doctor-sahib, Missi-sahib Victoria May sends this to you. She thinks you want to see it now." The doctor glanced curiously at Rama's excitement. There was nothing about delivering a letter to upset this young man, but it was apparent that he was upset, decidedly so. William glanced at the letter. When he saw the postmark his heart beat faster. Pennsylvania, U. S. A. This would be an answer to his plea for funds for the long-dreamed-of hospital.

" Doctor-sahib." Rama's voice was timid, he glanced covetously over his shoulder.

As William started to open the letter he realized that something was troubling the boy. Why did he glance toward the road? What caused his eyes to shine and his lips to tremble? William thrust the unopened letter into his pocket and turned to the business at hand.

" Rama," he fixed the youth with a mockingly stern eye, " something's on your mind."

" Yes, Doctor-sahib." William had expected an answering smile, but the dark face was grimly earnest.

William became alarmed. " What is it? You're feeling well, aren't you? "

Rama nodded, then licked his lips nervously.

" Now, now," said William kindly, " there's something on your mind. Let's have it."

Rama looked about to make sure they were not overheard, then whispered to the doctor. " It's a she," he stammered, gesturing awkwardly to the road outside the compound wall.

William was puzzled. " A she." He sincerely

hoped Rama had not been backsliding in his Christian teachings. "Just who are you talking about?" he asked, while the embarrassed young native squirmed uncomfortably while summoning up his courage.

"Come now, Rama." William put his hands on the boy's shoulders. "Surely it's not that bad." Then with deep understanding in his face he added, "You can tell me anything. Don't be afraid." His attitude reassured the young man, for he drew a big breath and began.

"This she," he indicated the blank wall again, "this she . . ." He blushed, then went on. "She approached me—for money." He lowered his dark eyes, ashamed. William drew a quick breath of relief and found himself marveling at the youth's attitude. Brought up in a background of nonchalant immorality, Rama had, in a few short months, grasped the pity and futility of cheap love.

"She approached me . . . so I brought her here," he concluded and William smiled at his solution.

"I see." The doctor stroked his beard, then ventured: "What are your plans for this ' she '?"

Rama lowered his head. "I—I should like to have her made a Christian," he admitted and with a trusting look put the whole affair into William's capable hands.

"Well, now, wait a minute," cautioned the doctor. "Has she—well, has she said she wanted to become a Christian?"

"No, Doctor-sahib," he said then his dark face

became bright. " But I should like for you to make her one." Rama stood on one foot, anxiously scanning the doctor's face.

William pondered. Rama's desire to be of help to his fellow humans should be encouraged. " Oh, well, bring her here to see me," he directed and Rama's face became as light as a Diwali light festival as he dashed out of the courtyard into the street to get " she."

Had William been able to look outside the courtyard walls he would have understood the reason for Rama's agitation. " She " had a name. It was Zizabai, and Zizabai was as sulky and as pretty a native girl as could be found in the Bombay Presidency. Her great, black eyes brooded out of a heart-shaped face the color of warm milk-cocoa. The continual chewing of much pahn had stained the full, small lips a brilliant red, while her youthful roundness was ill-concealed beneath a dirty but bright red sari. Zizabai had reason to sulk. She was a widow, and—which is most unusual in India—was resentful.

She had told Rama she was a widow, defiantly and boldly. And Rama's admiration of her had increased. He remembered a widowed aunt who'd suffered the punishment of every Indian bereaved wife. Her enforced servitude in the house of her husband's family, her relinquishment of all jewels and ornaments, and the never-ending insults of the mother-in-law who blamed her for the death of the husband were the usual fate of a widow. But the aunt had accepted her misfortune meekly, as Indian women have done for centuries.

But not Zizabai. "I ran away," she explained briefly and her pretty face showed her complete disdain for a deceased elderly husband, a nagging mother-in-law and Indian customs in general.

"It is because she has gone to school!" the mother-in-law had shrieked again and again, crying out against her daughter-in-law's radical behavior. "A woman must be obedient and industrious. She must never question." The age-old advice whizzed by Zizabai's lovely ears like a bulbul bird and she ran away.

And now the rebellious young widow found herself being hurried into the presence of a strange white man by a youth who called himself Rama. Zizabai looked at William; glowered.

Rama was explaining to her. "You become a Christian. Doctor-sahib make a good woman out of you."

Zizabai moved impatiently under her bright sari, rattled her anklets, spat pahn onto the verandah and snorted. William found it difficult to believe she was an Indian woman. She had none of their infinite patience and meekness. But she did have beauty. He began to understand Rama's interest.

"I never force Christianity upon anyone." William smiled, trying to ease her unruly mind. "Christianity must be a change in the heart," he explained. "It must come from within."

Zizabai's eyelids drooped. She was completely bored. Rama became anxious. "You can try to become a Christian, Zizabai," he pleaded.

She examined her bracelets which custom decreed taboo for a widow, then deliberately smiling into Rama's concerned face spoke.

"You like Zizabai?" The perfect white teeth glittered like Ceylon pearls in the sun.

Poor Rama flushed deeply at the brazenness in her voice and turned helpless eyes toward William. This is ridiculous, thought the doctor, and took a deep breath. Directing a kindly and what he hoped was an understanding look at the girl, he started to speak. Zizabai turned her head impudently, loudly spat pahn into the courtyard.

William's words died. He gritted his teeth, hesitated a moment, then called with sudden inspiration:

"Mary! Oh, Mary, will you come out here, please?"

Mary hurried out at her husband's call. It was not until she came onto the verandah, into the sunlight, that Zizabai's expression changed. The girl's sullenness disappeared. Her eyes grew wide as she watched the golden sheen of Mary's hair the beautiful eyes and the sweet mouth.

Mary looked from Zizabai to Rama to William. "Yes?" she questioned and her eyes filled with curiosity.

Before William could answer, Zizabai's voice sounded frank and unrestrained. "You pretty!"

she cried enthusiastically to Mary and impulsively moved to her side.

William watched his wife closely as she turned to the girl. Mary had a way with some of the native women, especially the sulky ones. He was eager to see how she worked. But Mary's method was not obvious. She merely looked at Zizabai, deep into the troubled black eyes, and smiled. Not a word, just a smile. William recalled that he had smiled, too, but by some unexplainable magic Mary's smile found reflection in Zizabai's face. The sullen, defiant expression lifted, and Rama and William glanced at each other briefly as a dark, spangled arm entwined itself about Mary's slim waist.

" She Christian? " Zizabai's question was abrupt. She asked it of William.

" Oh—yes, yes, of course," he answered, surprised by the sudden question.

Zizabai shifted the pahn about in her mouth, deliberating. Presently she spoke. " Then maybe I be Christian, too."

It was not until Mary had disappeared into the little dispensary with Zizabai and Rama, that William took the letter from his pocket. His hands shook slightly as he turned the letter over, inserted his thumb under the carefully-sealed flap. And then he paused. Suppose there were no funds? His letter to the Bryn Mawr church had been concise, yet filled with plans and figures for his dream. But could they know, those sheltered, safe and free people, of India's dreadful need? He'd explained in words, but words were only shadows of the cruel, depressing truth. Ten thousand dollars he had asked. Despondency gripped him. He felt a sharp desire not to read the letter. Until he knew, he would have hope. But what if they refused? William stirred angrily. " Where is your faith? " he asked himself and, gripping the envelope with a steady hand, tore it open.

He read the letter once, quickly without eye for details. And then he read again. Slowly this time, so as not to miss one word. And suddenly he let go a shout. " Mary! Mary! " There was laughter, exultation in his voice.

Together they read and reread . . . excitedly, joyously. " Ten thousand dollars! They're sending us ten thousand dollars! " Mary's voice held happy tears. William made no comment, but as he held her close she felt him tremble, and Mary knew his heart was much too full to speak even a word.

William was up early the next morning. As he dressed in his best suit and donned his *topee*, Mary knew he was going to make a special visit.

" Now," said the vigorous doctor to his wife, " I'll remind the Prime Minister of his offer of gratitude."

Mary stared. " You're going to ask him a favor? "

He nodded.

" But what is it? "

" Let me tell you when I return." He placed a quick kiss upon her forehead.

Mary smiled and shook her head. " You're going to get your hospital," she stated, her eyes filled with admiration. " You get everything you want, don't you, William? "

" No," he answered, going out the door, " just those things the Lord wants for me. But," he added, " I try to be mighty aware of those things."

In his richly carved business office, seated behind a massive teakwood desk, the Prime Minister listened to the plans of the amazing doctor from Canada; plans for a modern hospital on the twelve-acre site in Miraj.

In Miraj! The Prime Minister's heart beat high with pride. What a thriving, busy hospital would mean to the village! Patients seldom went to a hospital alone. They were usually accompanied by their immediate families and not infrequently by dozens of relatives, distant and otherwise. These people would have to live and eat. Business in Miraj would boom. The state official rubbed his hands together vigorously. He must tell his brother and his two uncles. They would buy up more property—build rest houses and a shop or two in the bazaar.

But a troublesome thought crossed his mind. " I understand," he mentioned with a careless gesture, " that you have been preaching at your dispensary."

William nodded.

" I trust," the Prime Minister added, " that you will not find this necessary at your new hospital."

His voice became smooth, ingratiating. " You see, we in India have many millions of gods. One more is really not necessary." His eyes gleamed sharply as he inclined his head.

William stiffened. It was imperative to obtain the cooperation of the State. The Prime Minister knew this, and William realized abruptly that the man was not favorable to the Christian teachings. The ten thousand dollar fund was of little use without official friendship. William glanced at the smug official, who reposed in his chair, toying with a tassel as silky as his smile. Suddenly William became impatient with cat-and-mouse methods. Bringing his closed fist down upon the teakwood desk, he spoke plainly.

" I'm sorry," his directness gave him courage, " but my hospital without His Word would be like a body with the life gone out of it. And I do not propose to erect a tomb, but a working, live organization."

Krishnaji Chandra pursed his lips. " I regret exceedingly your decision," he said in a sad, low voice.

" I can make no other." William set his jaw firmly under his brown beard.

The men looked into each other's eyes, gauging the other's strength. Then the Prime Minister relaxed, smiled, and leaned back in his chair.

" Very well." His hands folded outward gracefully. " Your desire shall be honored and your every request shall be my command."

William drew a deep breath of sheer relief. It

would be easier now. " The other day," he started,
" you offered to grant me a favor."

The Prime Minister bowed.

" Mr. Chandra," William smiled, " I have come to
ask two favors."

The eyes of the official twinkled. He secretly enjoyed the daring and courage of the Canadian doctor.
" Yes? "

" First, I would like to buy the twelve-acre site I
mentioned from the State of Miraj."

" It is granted," replied the official. " I shall see
that you obtain it for less than a reasonable fee."

" I have money to meet a fair price," rejoined
William.

Krishnaji Chandra nodded. " And the second
favor? " He was intrigued.

" The second is that you remove the people now
living on the land."

A puzzled look came over the Prime Minister's
face. " There are people living on that land? "

" Yes," said William. " People who are known as
untouchables."

An expression of relief flooded the official's round
face. His voice rippled with mirth. " Untouchables,
my good friend, are outcastes, lower than the lowest.
And I do not even consider them humans."

As William started to protest the stout man held
up a restraining hand. " Yes, yes, it shall be done.
I shall see to their removal."

His genial face held only promise of good-will, so

William did not pursue the problem further. After all, the Prime Minister was a man with principle. So William left the office in high spirits, blissfully unaware that in India a man may have principle but no concern whatever for the welfare of his fellow human beings.

8

WILLIAM'S HIGH spirits boiled up and ran over, rival-
ing the sun's rays in the living room of the bungalow.
Sitabai smiled delightedly over the brass trays containing the morning's chota hazri as she passed tiny
cups to Mary, William, and their early-morning
guest, Victoria May.

In spite of the older woman's usual frigidity, Mary
could see that Victoria May was almost as thrilled
and excited over the prospect of a hospital as she and
William. The perennial straw sailor quivered as the
prim woman listened excitedly to William's plans.

" Our first building will be a children's ward," he
anticipated, balancing the teacup on one knee. As he
spoke his words brought back poignant memories of
the little sister, Elizabeth. The same thought came to
Mary.

" Tell Victoria May about your sister," she suggested, crossing the room to replace a brilliant marigold which had fallen from its brass vase.

William needed no prompting. A sense of well-
being and power for accomplishment filled him. His
voice was mellow and sweet as he described the gift
of his sick sister. Mary looked fondly at her husband.
How he loved to tell that story. His brown eyes shone
as he told of building up the original sum to eight
hundred dollars, and how carefully he had saved it for

a purpose worthy of his little sister's sacrifice. Now that purpose was to be fulfilled.

"The first building to go up will be a children's ward. That eight hundred dollars should build it." His eyes looked tender. "We'll call it the Elizabeth Wanless Memorial!"

Victoria May sniffed, hastily wiped an errant tear from her eye. When this William Wanless becomes stirred, she thought, his powers of description are certainly eloquent.

"Listen!" Mary stood still. She had caught a strange sound. A sad, far-off wailing sound.

"That's odd," said Victoria May as she cocked her head, listened intently with her good ear.

Louder and louder the sound grew, like a great sea of lament rolling onto a brokenhearted beach.

"It's coming this way," announced William, and, putting aside the teacup, crossed to the front door and opened it wide. "I say!" he gasped.

Moving into the compound, immersed in various stages of misery, were scores and scores of dirty, ragged brown people. Hands fluttered helplessly in the air, wild cries went up, despairing fists beat upon crestfallen breasts. The crowd moved forward in deep, sodden misery.

"What do you suppose they want?" Mary could not keep the fear from her voice. The spectacle was so terrifying, so awful.

Again Mary squirmed under Victoria May's reprimand. "There's nothing to be afraid of," she criticized, but added as an afterthought, " I've never seen anything like this before. I wonder what they *do* want? "

But William neither questioned nor hesitated. Sensing human misery, he immediately made himself available for its relief. As he stepped onto the verandah the crowd surged forward, their terrible lamentations raised in a hymn of agony. Several threw themselves at his feet, prostrated with grief.

" Come now," William's good, common-sense voice served as a blotter for many tears, " what's this all about? Get up. Get up." He helped to their feet some of the prostrated ones. The sounds died down, but the misery deepened in their faces.

" Come now, lad." William comforted a shrieking little boy, frightened by the grief of his elders.

A hesitant spokesman stepped forward. " Doctor-sahib," he began, his head low, then broke off in extreme embarrassment. For he and his many friends were outcastes. This thing they were doing was daring and terrible.

Their fear and timidity touched William. His voice was as gentle as the soft beat of rain. " What is it you want to tell me? "

Grateful response showed on the fearful face before him. " Doctor-sahib," the man began again, but once more hesitated. He was about to do an unheard-of thing. Outcastes, miserable, foul untouchables, were about to register a complaint against their State. The man's agonized eyes filled with tears.

William walked to his side, put his arm about the thin shoulder. He felt the slender body shake as if with sickness. To be embraced as a brother! "Tell me what you have to say." The doctor felt an overwhelming joy that they had dared hope for his help.

The outcaste's eyes, gentle as those of a gazelle deer, stared helplessly into William's face. He murmured, like a child confessing sin to a beloved parent. "Our homes. This morning the officials come and destroy our homes. Now we have nowhere to go." His voice trembled, his gesture included the crowd in the compound. A soft, dismal whispering passed through the multitude.

William's brows puckered in conference. What did the man mean? "They destroyed your homes? You have nowhere to go?"

The unhappy outcaste nodded. "Yes, Doctor-sahib. They tell us you build fine new hospital, but why put us away from our homes? Where do we go? We are homeless."

An unhappy cloud hovered over the doctor's heart. That was the way the Prime Minister kept his promise. The heartbroken natives, gathering courage, told of the official's surprise visit early in the morning with elephants. How the people were driven from their huts, the elephants trampling the village, and the whole place destroyed.

"We ask them where do we go but they laugh and say, 'Doctor-sahib wants land for hospital.'" Tears again came to the dark eyes.

" Hmmm." William felt a swift surge of resentment against the callous official. And then a troublesome thought pricked him. Had the Prime Minister deliberately used these methods to show his disregard for Christian ethics?

Twenty minutes later William faced the State official across the latter's teakwood desk. Krishnaji Chandra received William with more than ordinary cordiality. His plump, well-dressed body bobbed about excitedly while his eyes held the delighted expression of a child awaiting praise for a task well done.

Is he sincere, William asked himself, or assuming this pose to make it more difficult for me? Well, he'd give the man the benefit of the doubt.

" My friend," the doctor's voice held sincerity, " I want to thank you with all my heart for your spirit of cooperation. But," here the sharpness of William's tone brought dangerous lights to the official's dark eyes, " I cannot accept your *method* of cooperation."

The little man spluttered. " You asked me to clear the land, my friend, and I have cleared the land! " His voice was injured.

William stared intently across the desk, spoke from his heart. " You know the purpose of this hospital, sir. I'm sure it's obvious to both of us that I cannot build upon the broken hearts and ruined homes of the outcastes."

A look of unhappiness settled upon the round, dark face. "I cannot please you," the Prime Minister fretted. "You are very hard to please, Doctor-sahib." There was vexation in his tone.

"I don't mean to be." William's sincerity impressed itself upon an unwilling subject. "I am only trying to serve my Master."

The peevish Indian fumed. "Your God is so demanding."

William continued eloquently. "There is one great command. That is Love. It solves all problems, simply and without complication. I don't call that demanding. In fact, I call it a release from the troublesome complications of gods which demand that we despise this man and look down on that man and divide all men into castes. But "—here William slacked his quickened tongue and smiled disarmingly—"I am not here to criticize or condemn. I wanted the land freed for my hospital and that you agreed to do. But—I do not want to see those dispossessed people without homes."

The official scowled childishly. "I don't know what else to do."

"Well," William's voice was irresistibly constructive, "it would cost very little to allot them another piece of ground and rebuild their homes for them. In fact, it would be an excellent opportunity to rebuild better homes."

The Prime Minister grunted, paced about his office. This doctor and his foolish ideas about caste and

Christianity! But—with the coming of the hospital there would be increased business, and his uncle had already bought two new stalls in the bazaar where he would sell cloth. To rebuild a few huts was not so much to ask in exchange for friendship with a progressive white man.

" Doctor-sahib," he said, and his face beamed with hastily-summoned cheerfulness, " your request shall be granted."

A frantic knocking at the office door caused both men to be startled.

Krishnaji Chandra, annoyed at this lack of respect, strode to the door and threw it open. A wide-eyed and perspiring Rama almost fell into the room. He salaamed hysterically before the Prime Minister, uttered abject apologies for his inexcusable behavior, then turned to William.

" Doctor-sahib," he quivered, " come to the dispensary quick! There is no time to lose." Rama shook with urgency, scarcely able to catch his breath.

" Calm yourself," advised William. " You're only wasting time. Now, what is it? "

" The Maharajah of Kolhapur! "

" The Maharajah? " The Prime Minister's voice became concerned.

" What's happened? " demanded William.

" Oh." Rama, realizing he had not explained, spoke rapidly. " His arm was hurt hunting wild boar."

" Badly hurt? " This from the native official.

William tried to piece the scattered information together. " Well, where is he? Does he need my help? "

" Yes, yes." Rama nodded so hard perspiration flew in drops from his face. " He is coming to the dispensary now! "

" Dr. Wanless," the Prime Minister's soft hand gripped William's arm. Honest anxiety shone in his eyes. " Take good care of my friend, the Maharajah."

William nodded reassurance. " I'll do my best," he promised and hurried to Sangli to prepare for the illustrious patient.

As he sped along the crude dirt road on his bicycle, William was busy trying to plan a bed which would hold His Highness. Only once had he glimpsed this Indian Monarch. It had been on an early morning, when William first discovered the twelve-acre site at Miraj. He had driven to it before starting work at the dispensary, when a great shout, the sound of trumpets and the thundering feet of trotting horses had proclaimed the approach of His Highness, bound on a hunting trip. Emerging mountain-like from among the dozens of horses, tongas, ekkas, and other conveyances, was a great, hulking elephant wearing a beautifully embroidered blanket of velvet. On it, swaying in his silver howdah, rode the stately Maharajah of Kolhapur. William remembered his first impression.

" He's the only man I ever saw who could diminish the size of an elephant."

And now William had to plan a bed for this giant monarch whose size was as fabulous as his wealth. And not only plan a bed for His Highness, but a place for his private retinue which would include at least forty people.

When William arrived at the dispensary the place was in a tumult. Mary, Victoria May, Zizabai and numerous native helpers were frantically clearing a space for the Maharajah's bed, sending to the bungalow for bedding and to the bazaar for delicate foods.

" Has he had a bad accident? " William asked of Mary.

" I don't know," she replied. " But from what his boy said he'll probably have to stay overnight at least."

William attacked the problem of a bed. Unlike his many native subjects who slept upon the floor, the Maharajah had adopted the European bed. William borrowed two charpoys. These rope beds, arranged together, would make one bed for His Highness. As Rama came panting into the buzzing dispensary, William put him to work and together they fashioned a most acceptable cot for size and added two thick mattresses for comfort. " Now if it only proves strong enough," thought the doctor.

Victoria May scurried into the building, her arms laden with bananas, oranges and some choice mangos.

" That terrible commotion down the street must

mean the Maharajah is coming." She hurried into the small kitchen cubicle.

" Ta, de-de-dah, de-de-dah! " Conch-shell bugles gave off their shrill notes which mingled weirdly with the calls of the elephant boys. " Chee! . . . Chee! " The huge elephant lumbered into view with flashing gold cords wound about his tusks. " Chee! . . . Chee! " The earth seemed to tremble outside the small dispensary as the mammoth beast came near, his royal burden swaying in the silver howdah.

As William hurried out the door he saw the members of His Highness' entourage helping the royal person to disembark. Weak from the loss of blood, his servants helped him climb down the ladder at the side of his faithful elephant.

As the Maharajah stood before him, William stared. The man must be six feet five, he thought, and estimated his weight between three and four hundred pounds. A long, flowing white shirt and white linen trousers topped off by an orange coat and green turban wound of ten yards of silk, made the Maharajah look like a towering Arabian Nights' figure. It was hard to believe he had not been conjured up out of the atmosphere.

But His Highness had a personality as expansive as his body.

Disdaining offers of a stretcher the great figure nodded courteously to William. " You are Dr. Wanless? " A voice like the low key on an organ sounded.

The Maharajah's First Meeting with Dr. Wanless.

" Yes, Your Highness," said William. " They tell me you've been injured." And with a glance at the huge arm which lay useless at its owner's side while matted and caked with blood, William continued. " Come in, please."

Mary watched the two men as they entered the dispensary. Her husband was not large in stature, and beside this giant of a man he appeared much smaller. But if one looked into their faces, Mary thought, William's had the strength of a giant, while the Maharajah's resembled a youthful, puckish boy.

Streams of anxious, talkative attendants clustered about His Highness, while the royal native doctor, who had attended the Maharajah on the trip, approached William in a calm, professional manner.

" He severed an artery with his spear," the trim native doctor explained while the Maharajah was being made comfortable on his improvised charpoy. " Fortunately I was able to check the flow of blood, but His Highness insisted upon further treatment at your hands. Your fame has spread wider than you know, Dr. Wanless," admitted the native doctor.

" You saved his life," commented William, examining the severed artery crudely tied by the native doctor. The Maharajah didn't seem to hear the conversation. His delighted eyes wandered about the room, peering at intriguing bottles. His nostrils sniffed the odor of disinfectant. William found himself amused. This royal being, this Maharajah of Kolhapur, was behaving exactly like a big, overgrown

child who had discovered to his amazement a new
wonder in his astonishing world.

It was obvious that His Highness was intensely
interested in hospital work and as he dressed the
wound, William explained the work at Sangli dispensary and also revealed his plans for the new hospital.

" My friend," boomed the Maharajah enthusiastically, " I shall make a handsome contribution toward your hospital! I shall ——" but his words were
interrupted by furious voices from the verandah.
The large monarch recognized the thin, flute-like
voice of one of his servants.

" There are no provisions for us here! I am
humiliated! "

Another voice wailed, " This place! It is not fit
for chickens! "

The Maharajah glanced at William, embarrassment and vexation covering his face. " My apologies," he murmured, then in a voice like a sudden
clap of thunder, roared out, " Quiet! Quiet, miserable ones, or I shall have you cut into bits and throw
your pieces to the pigs! "

Shocked exclamations from the verandah greeted
his words. The servants had not known His Highness would hear. With a few sharp squeaks they
hastily ran into the compound, overcome with shame.

" I apologize for my worthless servants," boomed
the Maharajah loudly enough for the departing ones
to hear. Then with a soft chuckle he added, " Pay

no attention to my flock, Dr. Wanless. They are spoiled, but then so am I." And with a hearty laugh he abandoned himself to the final ministering of William's skilful hands.

" A hospital," the huge man was heard to murmur later that evening. "A fine, new hospital." He turned to an attendant. " Tell the doctor I want to see him," he ordered. " Hurry . . . Hurry! "

William rushed to his bedside, fearful of a relapse. " Are you all right? " the doctor asked breathlessly.

" My friend," the impulsive monarch boomed, " I could not go to sleep without clasping your hands. A hospital . . . a hospital! It is a miracle! The people of my nearby State are in especial need. Now, with your new hospital so close, they can avail themselves of your surgical ability." His eyes sparkled. " I congratulate you, Dr. Wanless, and I congratulate India, and the Hindus, Mohammedans, Parsees, Jains and every other tribe, and especially do I congratulate the British Empire for giving us *you!* " The great, hairy paws nearly crushed William's hand, but he found himself smiling with genuine affection into the face of this huge, childlike, whimsical monarch.

❧ 9 ❧

THE DESOLATE, twelve-acre site, which had lain unwanted for centuries, now teemed with activity. A
new, vital, constructive way of life found expression
upon its rocky surface. Busy natives chipped away
all day to make uniform the size of great, quarried
rocks. Round and round went an aged ox, tied to a
pivoted stick which stirred mortar in a round trough.
Open buckets on the heads of women and boys conveyed this mortar to the foundation where slowly, but
accurately, the hospital took shape.

"Here, let me show you how to do that!" A
thousand and ten times William repeated this. "Let
me show you how." And with painstaking care and
inexhaustible patience the doctor demonstrated over
and over again the many and varied processes which
went into the construction of the building.

"William, where did you learn how to build a hospital?" asked Mary curiously. She had first learned
of his ingenuity when it was discovered that native
architects were unable to draw satisfactory plans for
the medical center. William eagerly sought their
help, but the answer was always the same. "No,
Doctor-sahib, we cannot build according to *your* desires. Our instructions are here." And they in-
variably opened the ancient Indian books of archi-
tectural construction based upon the supposed desires

of their gods. " No. The gods would become angry were we to plan a building contrary to their wishes." William sighed over their bondage to superstition then set to work to draw up plans of his own.

" Now, if I can just find a good contractor . . ." Mary remembered the morning her husband had voiced that wish. Drawing the plans had taken so much of his time, if there was only someone available to take the responsibility of building. It would mean buying the materials, hiring workmen, supervising the work. Mary also remembered the morning he had said to her, " There is no contractor capable of supervising the building."

" You mean—it can't be built? " The incredulous thought seemed sacrilegious.

When he answered William's voice sounded more determined than ever. " It will be built. I'll be my own contractor."

She had started to voice a protest. His regular schedule was so heavy. Perhaps he planned on giving up his medical practice during the building?

But no. That wasn't the answer. " I shall do both," he explained and Mary wondered how he could possibly squeeze forty-eight hours' work into twenty-four, although she knew that he always accomplished whatever he undertook to do.

" Looks to me as if that building is never going to take shape," fussed Victoria May and reached for more bandages to wind.

" Oh, it isn't that bad," answered Mary, trying to keep a cheerful note in her voice.

" It's been a solid year and a half. And that husband of yours is working himself to death!" She emphasized her statement by jabbing a pin into a coiled roll of bandage.

Mary sighed. William was not only his own architect and contractor, he was also head carpenter, head plumber and head painter. It was he who had made a survey for the foundations and ordered stones from the quarry; he who had supervised the work and settled each petty and annoying problem that arose.

" Why wasn't the mortar-grinding ox fed yesterday? Why wasn't he given water?" Indolent workmen shrugged brown shoulders and left the question unanswered. " Where is the man who was responsible for spreading the mortar on the stones?" No one knew. " He is gone to his cousin's, Doctorsahib." Another said, " He is sick." Still another: " His wife's foot is heavy." To William that expression for pregnancy always smacked of humor. Petty thieving, prevarication and other annoyances scraped raw the nerves of the man whose principles were built on a foundation as simple and strong as that of his hospital.

" William, where did you learn to do all this?" Her husband's knowledge of building was a complete surprise to Mary.

" Well," he paused a moment, then answered, " I used to help my father. He was a good contractor

and carpenter. And when I worked in his hardware
store I learned about tools and types of construction.
But I guess the thing that helps me most is the fact
that the Lord *wants* a hospital built here.''

First the children's ward. A simple, attractive
bungalow encircled with wide verandahs and lovingly
shadowed by hastily-planted hibiscus, palms, tiny
acacia trees and vines which would blossom later with
red and yellow flowers.

'' Elizabeth Wanless Memorial.'' The words stood
out in large letters over the doorway.

'' I can't believe it's finished,'' breathed Mary to
William as they stood in the yard and looked at the
newly-completed ward.

'' Whack . . . whack . . . whack . . . whack.'' All
day long workmen chipped at the granite blocks for
the main building. William had divided his workmen into two crews. One group busied themselves on
the children's ward while the other built the large hospital proper.

'' We'll have no formal dedication service for this
building,'' William had said with the completion of
the Elizabeth Wanless memorial ward. '' It seems
more fitting that its dedication should consist of
simply opening the doors and gathering in the sick
children.'' But Mary noticed that he did more than
that. Early in the morning, on the day of its opening,
she saw William hang a picture in the hallway. The
face was that of a pretty girl of twelve who had dedi-

cated her pennies for " children who need them more
than I do."

As the last child patient was tucked into the last of
twelve tiny cots, Victoria May arrived to see the
filled ward, and for the first time since her arrival in
India Mary saw the older woman's eyes fill with
tears.

Neat as little brown-headed pins each carefully
slipped into its individual pin cushion were the children. The clean, white, airy room lined on each side
by well-spaced cots, the cloud-white sheets and the
flower-red blankets gave a feeling not only of cleanliness, but of warmth and well-being.

Into Victoria May's mind flashed her memory of
countless native children much like these, but wallow-
ing in dirt, neglected or subject to mystifying incan-
tations of superstitious holy men. Babies left on the
roadside to die; little girls thrust into lonely forests;
sick, suffering children whose bodies were beaten
fiendishly to relieve them of devils and evil spirits.
Victoria May's swimming eyes caught the dimpled
smile of a pert, tiny girl patient and she felt that a
time had come for decision. Straightening her straw
hat, she announced: " I want to work in this hospital.
I want to help in this work." And Mary, seeing her
tears, felt the kindness in the flinty older woman and
sensed beneath her stern demeanor, a heart of love.

Mary smiled and put her arm about Victoria May.
" I'm so glad," she whispered.

An impulse overcame Victoria May. " Mary,"

there was apology in her voice, " when you first came here . . ."

But Mary stopped her. " I know."

" You do? " For some reason the older woman seemed surprised.

Mary nodded. " But we'll be friends now, won't we? "

In answer the prim, methodical missionary gave way to her corked-up emotions and planted such a vigorous kiss on the young woman's cheek that Mary could not help thinking of a woodpecker.

As the main hospital building slowly took shape another bungalow was started. This was to be William and Mary's residence. As soon as it offered sufficient shelter the young couple took leave of the Sangli missionary compound and took up residence in the bungalow which was to be home to William in the busy years that followed.

The building of the hospital was annoyingly slow. The doctor often gritted his teeth and wondered why those whom progress benefited most often stood in its path. Indolence, thieving, apathy, were the work-men's chief characteristics. The work seemed to crawl. William accepted it as a challenge to his patience and remarked to Mary: " This experience is giving me some insight into the infinite patience of the Lord."

" How so? " asked his ever-attentive wife.

" Even at the snail's pace we're going, the hospital should be completed within the year, but think of the Lord's Kingdom on earth. Why, He's been waiting for hundreds of centuries for sinners to start building, and even now it doesn't look as if we've gotten around to laying one good, firm cornerstone for that Kingdom. By George! " William exclaimed with tremendous admiration. " How He continues to love us and keep His patience is more than I'll ever understand! "

How her husband could continue his medical practice and supervise the building of the hospital was what Mary could never understand. Of course, he was methodical. She noticed that William never made a waste motion. Every moment was made to count.

" William uses Time for his servant," she remarked to Victoria May and the older woman nodded. " He uses Time for his servant. That describes William Wanless to a ' T.' "

Finally, the long-dreamed-of hospital at Miraj was completed. As it stood straight and firm, anchored securely upon the rocky land, Mary wondered: " Could it be that this place, built in His name and for His service, is part of a cornerstone for His Kingdom on earth? "

She didn't broach the idea to William, knowing that he would be much too humble to consider seriously such a suggestion.

While Miraj teemed with activity, an evil, destructive force slowly gathered its formidable strength and prepared to crush western India; a force which was to offer discouragement and a burning challenge to the doctor who dared bring new ideas to a country whose beliefs were as static as its centuries-old temple carvings. An occasional foreboding rumble ruffled the calm. " Too much sun." " We must have rain." " The crops are dying." " In other villages people are beginning to go hungry."

William's alert and attentive ears caught the reports. He had been aware of the long period of hot sun, and the lack of rain. He had watched the native farmers with their primitive wooden hand plows attempting to break through the unyielding, baked soil. He had watched them prostrate themselves before the elephant-headed god, Ganesh, begging, praying for rain. " Rain, great Ganesh, rain! " " Ganesh, god of the harvest, son of the mighty Siva, rain . . . rain." " Thy mighty head is our sheaves of corn, thy graceful ears the winnowing basket, thy round stomach our overflowing barns . . . mercy on us, great Ganesh." But the carved, grinning Ganesh stared unseeing and unfeeling from his many shrines as patient, already hungry mothers fried the last chappati for their husbands and sons. They watched with helpless despair as the tiny green shoots of wheat and millet burned brown and drooped toward the hard earth. " Rain . . . rain," the worshippers implored, but Ganesh only grinned vacantly.

And now on the roads appeared a few straggling wanderers; grimly-gaunt men, quiet, suffering women, feeble, dying aged, and sickly children. It was the children who caused Mary's heart to cry out. William had found such a one on the road, deserted by friends and family, lying weakly waiting for death.

"Oh, God!" The exclamation was torn from Mary's throat. It was not blasphemy, but a prayer for strength to endure the sight of child starvation. That stomach! That grotesque, bulging stomach which loomed and leered like a mocking taunt; yet was starkly empty as a drum. The tiny protruding rib bones; skinny, knobbled legs with shamelessly revealed bone-structure; and above all the eyes . . . blameless, innocent, suffering, not understanding— yet not condemning . . . the awful, conscience-stabbing eyes of a starving child.

The little one had evidently come far. That meant there was famine in the north, fear of famine closing in gradually down the coast.

At Miraj the grotesquely shriveled little famine victim gratefully died. And on the same day an air of festivity invaded the inhabitants of the village. After two years of grueling, painstaking work, the wonderful new hospital was finished, and today marked its important ceremony of dedication. The huge Maharajah of Kolhapur, the portly Prime Minister of Miraj, the influential Rajah of Miraj, state officials, important personages and hundreds of in-

terested natives were already headed in the direction
of a stony, twelve-acre site upon which a miracle of
building had taken place.

During that morning, before the arrival of the
guests, William permitted himself the luxury of an
hour in which to do nothing but look upon the building of his dream. As he gazed upon its naked new-
ness the heavy, grey stone blocks took on a beauty
which for him no Taj Mahal could ever possess. Let
the romantic-minded extol the beauties of the lace-
like marble carvings, the fabulous pearl inlay and the
shimmering physical beauty of the Taj at Agra, but
William could not forget that it was a tomb, and that
its builder was a man of merciless and reckless
violence. Upon the worship of the dead and with the
life-labor of slaves a thing of physical beauty may be
built, thought William, but upon such a foundation
the Kingdom can never rest. He drew a deep breath
and went into the building, admiring the walls built
two feet thick to defy both heat and dampness. Firm,
easily-cleaned cement floors stretched throughout
the building which provided space for sixty beds. As
he turned into the male surgical ward William discovered Mary and Victoria May hastily spreading
new, white iron beds with fresh sheets. Mary looked
at the expression in her husband's face. She walked
to him, grey eyes glowing. "It's too good to be
true," she whispered, and William pressed a soft kiss
upon her cheek. Together they wandered through
the two stories of quiet, expectant rooms; a ward for

eye cases; two private single wards; two offices; the
male and female surgical wards with fourteen waiting
beds each; the male and female medical wards each
with ten beds; a laboratory, a linen room, four bath-
rooms and large, adequate hallways.

Through the wide windows in the female medical
ward William could see an object which was the pride
of the new institution. What a stir it had created
upon arrival! Workmen spread the news to their
friends, curious villagers rushed to the compound,
even the Maharajah of Kolhapur had made a special
trip to Miraj to gaze upon the wonders of an American windmill. It was the first windmill the villagers
had ever set their eyes upon and the tall, graceful iron
props and the huge wheel which whirled in the wind
caused the village to buzz with awe and speculation.
The Doctor-sahib said it was to pump water! With
the help of the great wheel the wind would pump
water for the hospital! Not since a village grandfather had the good fortune to die in sanctity at
Benares on the banks of the far-distant Ganges had
there been such a stir in Miraj. The Doctor-sahib
had explained that this windmill which came from
America was to supply water to sixteen different
places in the building. Large iron tanks installed
under the roof were to keep twelve hundred gallons
of water constantly on hand. Grizzled ancients shook
their heads. It was foreign magic. It was not for
India. The old ways were the best. They grumbled
among themselves and glowered at the windmill with

illy-concealed disfavor. But younger Indians questioned, tried to understand. As he painstakingly
explained its operations the doctor rejoiced that
young India asked questions and was developing a
thriving curiosity about new and better ways to live,
in spite of their parents' opposition.

William's brief perusal of the hospital was soon
interrupted by the arriving dignitaries. A heterogeneous assortment of vehicles crowded the road to
Miraj that day. The glittering, sparkling carriages
of state officials; the double-seated ekkas; a few
tongas; several crude wheeled vehicles drawn by
scraggly bullocks, and finally the arrival of the magnificent Maharajah of Kolhapur and his inevitable
entourage gaily splotching the dull road with every
color at the command of color-loving India.

The Prime Minister, his avaricious cousins and
bargaining uncle circulated, fawningly, among the
guests complimenting the Doctor-sahib in loud tones,
then huddling into whispered business sessions with
hawk-nosed friends. Victoria May and the dignified
Rajah of Miraj found an unexpected common interest
in their enthusiasm for the beloved Queen of the
Empire, Victoria. " The most wonderful woman in
history! " stated the Rajah and Victoria May added,
" And she was so happy with her Albert. What a
pity he had to die. She never remarried. I didn't
expect she would." And the Rajah nodded sympa-
thetically. " You know," Victoria May admitted
with a prim blush, " I was named after Queen Vic-

toria." She glowed with pride and the Rajah looked as if he was going to fall at her feet in worship.

Mary, her face flushed with happiness, circulated through the increasing crowd remembering every name, every face. She glanced at William. His glad heart had jumped up into his eyes. As he greeted each guest with hearty words of welcome his personality vibrated through the room and seemed to permeate the new building. He was Miraj hospital— Miraj hospital was William Wanless.

And then the dedication ceremony commenced. The Rajah was presented with a silver key with which he unlocked the front door. Short speeches were made by notables. Ezekiel Greyson, resplendent in a new grey suit, spoke with unaccustomed eloquence.

" This hospital is to be a demonstration of God's love to suffering mankind by the use of God's gift of scientific medical knowledge; an institution in which Jesus Christ, the Master Physician, makes known his saving power and grace in works of love, sympathy and mercy. Such an institution is the object of those who are responsible for this great building at Miraj."

William listened attentively—while his life seemed filled to overflowing with promise. He thought of the work ahead; the filling of the wards, the use of his up-to-date, efficient operating theatre, the new equipment which made right care possible.

A large round of applause sounded. Mr. Greyson

sat down. Then the Rajah of Miraj spoke the important words of the day. Standing beside a draped tablet his words were brief, but his voice held pride.

" On this day, July 4, 1894, I declare this hospital open." With a quick gesture he unveiled the marble tablet which proudly bore on its white face a detailed inscription of gratitude to those responsible for the erection of Miraj hospital, while under this appeared words which carried a poignant appeal:

> " Inasmuch as ye have done it unto one of the least of these my brethren, ye have done it unto me."

" Perhaps it's wrong to feel so elated," the doctor considered for he knew his face radiated with satisfaction, but his hospital meant obstacles overcome, faith rewarded, prayers answered, and a busy, fruitful future tugging at his eager heart.

As he glanced out a nearby window onto the road, his eyes fell upon several straggling travelers. And then a tiny, stumbling child with distended stomach came into view. Famine sufferers! A sharp chill touched the doctor. The idea of famine had seemed remote during the activity of building, but William realized that now it was no longer remote, but very close. He glanced at his wife. She, too, was staring through the window. Then of a sudden, as if drawn by an irresistible magnet, the heads within the new building turned and looked upon the wayfarers upon the road.

A quiet, unspoken panic seemed to grip everyone. For the first time came realization that famine was edging its insidious way into the village. As long as there had been *something* to eat, some supplies in the house, there had been no fear. But supplies were low, fields brown. The appearance of these gaunt, grim travelers took on a personal significance. The dedication ceremony continued, but it was as a fleck of foam upon a deeply surging tidal wave. Words issued from lips of speakers, but hearts strained with fear and dread. Here was famine . . . more lingeringly cruel than any plague and vicious, too. For famine would breed distrust, hate, covetousness, lying, stealing, cheating . . . and murder. Neighbors cast quick, oblique glances at one another, while a veil of distrust slowly rolled down over their minds. Which man of them had food and which had not? Who would live? . . . who would die? In that bitter, fearful instant friends became unspoken enemies.

That evening, which William had expected to enjoy in a quiet, satisfied perusal of the afternoon's dedication ceremony, was turned into a period of tense, apprehensive conference.

Mary, Victoria May and William grouped about the desk in his new office, trying to think through this new, formidable challenge. How could they meet this fresh disaster so swiftly approaching!

" When I first came to India there was famine." Victoria May reminisced and her severe face looked tight and drawn. " I prayed then that it would never, never come again. I'd rather battle any trouble in the world except hunger."

Mary thought of the distorted stomachs of children, the burning, dying planted fields of Miraj. The stealthy thing crept slowly, but inevitably. She felt no power to cope with it. " William, what are we going to do? "

The desperate eyes of the two women turned to the doctor. Finally he spoke. " In our own wisdom there *is* no answer," he said. But strangely enough his face was not afraid.

Later, in her own room, Mary uttered from the depths of her heart, " Give me faith, Lord. Give me faith like my husband's."

10

" WHERE IS the answer to our prayers?" Mary
feared to doubt, but facts could no more be ignored
than the beating Indian sun. Miraj had its hungry,
and every day there were more.

Mary watched the calm, confident face of her husband as he went about his never-ending work in the
immaculate new hospital. How could he be so completely unconcerned about this terrible famine which
was coming upon them? After all, one had to use
one's common sense.

" William," she approached him with more spirit
than she had used since suggesting the Taj Mahal
visit, " what are you going to do about the famine? "

The doctor stopped unpacking precious bottles of
chalmoogra oil for the lepers from Bombay long
enough to gaze curiously at the small, indignant figure
before him.

" Why, Mary," he answered, " that's an odd
question."

" Odd? " Mary echoed, and William noticed her
nervousness and uneasiness. " Do you call it odd that
I should trouble you as to whether the village is going
to starve to death? " Tears trembled on her eyelids,
she bit her lip, vexed at the unusual sarcasm in her
voice.

William, who seemed to move in a cloud of disinfectant these days, approached his wife with concern. " Mary," his voice was gently chiding, " where is your faith? " He was surprised as she shrugged her shoulders impatiently.

" I'm tired waiting! " she cried. " We can't just stand and do nothing! "

" But we're praying."

Praying, Mary thought, but why don't we get an answer? At that moment she was just a little bit unhappy about William. He'd always been such a man of action. Now, of all times, why must he do nothing?

" I can't act without guidance." William's voice held assurance, but it only irritated Mary.

" Well," she finally blurted, " if you won't do anything, I will! "

" What do you intend to do? " he asked. Perhaps the answer would come through Mary. William listened intently, eagerly.

" Ohhh," her voice trailed off. If she could only fall back on her indignation, but it had a miserable habit of deserting her when she needed it most. Mary collapsed on the nearest chair and wept.

" Now, now . . ." William was at her side. She looked tired, worried, he thought. She's been working too hard. He'd have to see that she had a rest.

She caught his two hands in hers, pressed them to her wet face.

" William." If she could only stop crying. She must tell him now. Right now. " William! " The

urgency in her voice caused him no little alarm. He
bent down, stared into her face. "Yes, Mary?"
There was anxiety in his voice now, and somehow it
was gratifying to Mary. Now she could tell him.

"William . . ." She looked into his face, tried
to hold back her tears. "I think, I believe,—oh,
William, I *know* we're going to have a baby!" And
she broke into heavy sobs.

William's hands gripped her shoulders. "We're
. . . ?" He caught his breath. He felt as if he
were being lifted off his feet with sheer joy. "Mary!
This is no time to cry!" He could have shouted.

She stared up at him hotly. "Why? Why isn't
it?" Angry flames in her eyes dried up the tears.
"I'm going to have a baby and you're going to let
us all starve to death!" There, now she'd told him
everything.

A smile touched William's lips, a smile as gentle
as the glow of an earthen lamp. As she looked into
her husband's adoring eyes, in spite of her anger
Mary felt the mystical charmed rapture of a bride.
She and William were to share a wonderful adventure. A growing sense of frustration and drabness
fell from the expectant mother and with the quick-
ness of Indian dawn she felt herself clothed in
radiance.

A shocking terror abruptly descended upon the
village of Miraj. Although crops were dying and
food supplies were low, violence had been absent from

the village. But with the coming of a hot May morning, fear of famine struck. During the night grim, hungry men had stolen into the home of a wealthy merchant. When morning came the foully murdered bodies of the merchant, his wife, son and servant lay in gruesome heaps while his store of wheat and rice were gone.

The villagers trembled. Those who " had," locked their doors, kept night sentinels beside their homes; while those who " had not " roamed the streets and brooded on their dying crops. And still no rain.

With the agony of thirst green things turned brown. Bushes, flowers, trees, crops . . . all were gathered in a mighty, withering harvest, by Death.

" Doctor-sahib, food . . . food! " More stood in the courtyard every day. William's impulse was to give. But of what lasting value could that be in the face of endless starvation? " Food! Food! "

" Lord God," the perspiration dropped from William's forehead as he prayed, " show me Thy way. There must be an answer somewhere—somehow! "

Because the crops died the farmers had no money, and because the farmers had no money the artisans could sell no wares. Brassmakers, pottery makers, weavers, jewelers, letter writers, sandal makers, all were hungry, for there was no rain.

Zizabai brought news to Mary. " They leave," she said, and pointed to the dusty road leading from

Miraj. A pitiful stream of hungry villagers, who had heard a rumor of work and food in far-off Bombay, straggled past the hospital. Mary could be silent no longer.

"William!" Her husband, coming from the busy operating room after a delicate spinal operation, looked tired and worn. Mary took him onto a side verandah, facing the highway, and pointed to the hungry leaving Miraj. "They'll only die." She was trembling. "They'll never get food anywhere else."

William looked at the pitiful group. There was a friendly farmer who had given him a sack of grain when his only son was snatched from death by him; a patient grandfather who had brought toys for the children's ward; a woman, heavy with coming life, laboring slowly behind her small, already hungry family. These were his people. They were hungry. And death would claim them on a hostile highway.

There was only a moment's hesitation, then William strode toward the road, his white surgeon's gown spreading like the wings of a huge bird.

"Wait!" His voice was commanding. The stragglers paused, stared at him with dull, hopeless eyes. As William looked into their pinched faces all discretion went from him. Throwing out his arms in a great, wide gesture he shouted at the top of his lungs. "Food! Food! *Food!*"

Heavy-lidded eyes snapped open. Hunger-wearied bodies quivered. For the briefest second they paused, as if unwilling to trust their very ears. And then

The maiden after a bath, seated on her stool at the spring just the great bath

The doctor, after a hectic moment or two, started the queue
past the grain sacks.

pandemonium. With a mighty shout the starving surged into the compound; red, blue, white, green, pink and orange garments fluttered about thin forms while fierce, eager faces massed in a heterogeneous formation to reach the building.

Food! Food!

Quicker than the rat-flea that carried the dreadful plague, the good news of available food spread into the village. Food at the hospital! Women grabbed up naked children, merchants dashed from deserted bazaar stalls, ancient grandfathers climbed upon the strong backs of grandsons and all joined the throngs pressing toward the hospital of the miracle-working Doctor-sahib.

"Bring grain from the storehouse!" ordered William to native servants who soon staggered back under the great sacks of rice. Zizabai plead with the crowd to line up—the Doctor-sahib would see that each received a handful of rice, but the eager ones climbed into the hospital windows, pushed open doors, swarmed about the kitchen snatching at every stray grain.

"A double handful to each," instructed William of two brown servants each standing over a bag of rice. With a roar the crowd surged forward. "Stand in line! In line!" called out the doctor, and after a hectic moment or two started the orderly file past the grain sacks.

The courtyard gradually emptied. Dark eyes twinkled and mouths spread in anticipatory smiles while laughter sounded in Miraj. Quicksilver gossip and cheerful quips tipped the merry conversation in a village which had been growing increasingly glum. As the last handful of grain was given out, Victoria May made a caustic comment: " If you're not careful, William Wanless, you'll be taken into the Hindu Pantheon as another of their thirty million gods."

As the final grateful one departed down the village road toward home, William looked at the empty sacks, then at his helpers, all drooping with the heat, and all so tired their eyes rolled foolishly in their heads. As they gazed on one another their full plight struck them. They had just given away the last sack of rice in the face of an oncoming famine, and here they stood, tired, dirty, hot. They had reached rock bottom. There was only one thing left to do and they did it. Somehow the deep, deep wells of laughter, bubbling beneath weariness and despair, released in full their delightful essence and upward it shot quivering, dancing through the tired bodies of the little group facing calamity. The tears coursed down their cheeks as they clung to each other and laughed and laughed.

The starkness of the situation became apparent in the light of early morning. As the dawn came, villagers filed into the hospital compound. The Doctor-sahib had given them food the night before . . . he would give them food for their breakfasts.

William heard their voices; saw their growing

number. He groaned. There was no sign of rain, no
more food in the hospital, and only a small amount of
money left to buy more. True, Northern and Eastern
India had no drought, crops there were good. But in
Southern and Western India where the crops had
dried up there was no money for the farmers; no
money for the artisans; no money for food.

As Mary stepped to the door of her husband's office,
she heard his voice low and deep; knew he was praying. She saw the milling, hungry crowd outside and
suddenly realized the enormity of William's problem.
And he was trying to solve it as the Lord wanted it
solved. Her actions of the previous day engulfed her
in remorse. William needed her love and understanding now more than ever before. Throwing open
the door of the office, she ran to him and in a moment
they were clasped in a close, unspoken embrace.

Neither heard the noise of the tonga as it drew up
before the hospital compound. Neither saw the
haughty Indian dispatch his servant from the vehicle
with a quick command. But both heard the rap upon
the outer door. William was there first. As the
doctor appeared in the doorway the Hindu in the
tonga smiled and drew back so he would remain un-
observed. The fastidious servant offered William a
scroll and a small leather purse.

" For you, Doctor-sahib." He salaamed graciously
and turning faded through the villagers in the compound, out into the tonga which quickly departed.

As William unrolled the scroll Mary hovered about

curiously. " What do you suppose it is ? " she asked, her eyes bright. " And that purse looks like it might have money in it."

" Probably a donation of some sort," murmured the doctor, unrolling the scroll. He held it out and together they read the carefully written Marathi.

" My most courteous greetings to a Christian gentleman. Will you kindly accept my poor gift and permit me to ask that you use it at your discretion, perhaps in the building of a hospital for unfortunate lepers."

The scroll was signed " anonymous," but the little purse contained a three thousand rupee note.

Mary moaned. " Build another hospital *now?* " she exclaimed. But before she could say another word William's voice rang out with joyous passion. " Thank you, Lord! Thank you! "

She stared at him. His face was eager; full of plans.

" William! What do you mean? " she said.

" Mary," he exulted, " this is our answer! "

" Answer? " echoed Mary, unable to understand how the building of a leper hospital would answer the challenge of the famine.

William explained as patiently as his enthusiasm would permit.

" If the villagers have money they can buy food. The grain merchants here still have some for sale. Then we'll bring some in from Northern and Eastern India. Now—the natives can earn this money by their labor, building the new leper home, don't you see?"

The idea gradually unfolded before Mary. "But is there enough money here?" She indicated the anonymous gift.

"There will be!" William's voice rang with assurance. "I'm writing now to the British Mission to Lepers. Why, this idea will have meaning for people! They'll want to help us!"

If Mary, in a moment of annoyance, had accused her husband of lack of activity, she rescinded it now. William's actions resembled nothing less than a sweeping monsoon. Enthusiastic letters were dispatched to England with the whole plan written in glowing terms.

The most pressing problem was a site for the leper home. Obviously it was not desirable to have it too near the hospital. William lost no time in contacting the fabulous Maharajah of Kolhapur. Did the Maharajah have a suggestion as to a site for this great, new undertaking? The Maharajah certainly did. The ardor of the doctor stirred the monarch's imagination and he presented the Canadian missionary with a perfect spot of land just two miles from the hospital proper.

Making known his plan to the villagers, William lost no time in starting to build. Every needy man and woman was given work to do. The wages were necessarily small, but enough to buy food and ward off starvation. Orders for grain were sent to Bombay and almost immediately the great, life-giving sacks started to arrive, supplementing the village grain-merchants' dwindling supply.

Gruesome and terrible tales of the famine in other villages came to the ears of Miraj residents, and with gratitude in their hearts to the great Doctor-sahib who had saved them from death, they worked unsparingly. In the eyes of many snatched from the edge of starvation, William took on the qualities of a god. He had done what even their great Ganesh had failed to accomplish. He made it possible for them to get food. With returning strength they were again a contented people and their gratitude knew no bounds.

Gradually the leper home took shape. The purpose of the building spurred many to build conscientiously and eagerly, for no man knew who would next be claimed by the loathsome, rotting disease. Mothers remembered beloved children who had been thrust from the village to wander miserably about the country calling " unclean, unclean," and eventually to die as despised and rejected beggars.

But the Doctor-sahib meant to turn this new home over to those so afflicted, to give them love and care. A great curiosity developed about the God for whom this Doctor-sahib toiled so unceasingly. True, the philosophy of the more exalted of their own gods was similar in some respects to the " white man's God," but He had something new to offer; something that was finding a true, deep response in the hearts of gentle, friendly people. This new God taught of Love. And India needed Love.

Babies once threatened with starvation now grew plump and merry. The streets were filled once more with giggling, doe-eyed little girls and saucy boys. Bazaar stalls again filled with bargaining customers, while at the rapidly-building leper home a spirit of constructive hope prevailed. Indian men and women, under the direction of the wondrous Doctor-sahib, had come face to face with their ancient, harrowing enemy of famine and with the strength of their bodies and faith of their hearts had driven the cursed one from the village. It was no longer necessary to bow one's head helplessly as a dumb animal in the face of disaster. Good could come out of evil. People were made to live, not to die. Hope bloomed in the faces of the villagers of Miraj and a contagious, vigorous spirit of life coursed through the veins of the town, making it a place of new hope for all of India.

And then came the rains. Fast and hard and even the furious drops pelted the streets and fields. Good, stinging, fresh rain. The poor withered earth sucked greedily. Oxen relaxed in bovine placidity as the water trickled down their faces, over their dusty backs. Rollicking, festive, and with fierce joy natives wallowed in the damp, oozing mud. Soon there would be crops, but most important of all—the villagers of Miraj would be alive to enjoy them. William looked out his window at the rain; drew strength from its cool blessing.

But India had not thrown down her greatest challenge.

The country stirred and quivered with the coming of the Vitoba Mela, when up from the musty depths of centuries came the worship of this incarnation of the great god Vishnu. Unlike the Kartik Festival in worship of the four-armed Goddess Kali whose mouth with her long, lolling tongue called out for blood sacrifice, the Festival of Vitoba brought pilgrims who prostrated themselves before the idol at Pandarpur and joined in bloodless worship for eight days.

But traveling with the pilgrims and spreading death over their line of march were germs of dreaded cholera.

And like the Goddess Kali, Mother Cholera called aloud for sacrifice—a sacrifice of blood.

11

MARY'S SCRAPBOOK was spasmodic. It held clippings
from Canadian newspapers about her husband, news
items from the Bombay paper about the work of the
Miraj hospital and sometimes statistics or brief confi-
dences in her own handwriting. She was writing as
the rain fell in soothing regularity.

"As the Indian women say, my 'foot has been
heavy' and I somehow feel that today will be my
time. Zizabai and Victoria May refuse to leave me
alone and I'm afraid some of the really sick patients
at the hospital are being somewhat neglected.
William has had everything ready for a week now.
I'm certain he is as excited as I am. Sitabai says my
Indian friends are praying for a boy, but I have no
preference. I do wish papa could be here to see his
first grandchild and also to see William's great work.
Papa was right about William being a dreamer, but
he's also a doer, which papa didn't know when he
objected to our marriage. I'm sure if we had stayed
in Toronto they would have been the best of friends,
for William would no doubt have been one of the
greatest surgeons in Canada. But he's so happy here,
and everyone loves him. I think I'm right about
today being my day. I'd better send for William."

William was not far away. The news spread
quickly. It is the Wanless mem-sahib. News spread

with the lightning-fast rapidity of tongues attuned to gossip. Every event happening in the village belongs to each villager. Indians have no secrets one from the other. Bright, sari-clad figures flashed from door to door. " It is the Doctor's mem-sahib."

Tiny boys and girls ran at their mothers' heels, children who had been brought into the world healthy and uncontaminated because of Mary's work among the mothers. As excitement spurred women toward the hospital, many tongues clicked reminiscently of the early attempts of the Doctor-sahib and his wife to abolish the practices of the ignorant midwives and train women to deliver babies intelligently. But many women still shook their heads, preferring the ancient methods of confinement on the bare, dung-washed floor with the old customs of the village dais instead of the advanced, sanitary ways of the scientific West. And now the mem-sahib was to have her turn. But was she not fortunate? She would be attended by her own husband, the miracle-working Doctor-sahib.

The usual courtyard group of relatives and friends of hospital patients grew and swelled with the coming of the native women. " What would the child look like? " " Would it be a boy child? " " What would they name it? " " Would it be white at birth or brown like their own children? " The excitement and restlessness in the courtyard grew as several eyes sighted the white-gowned figure of the Doctor-sahib rush by an open window. Some had thought to bring pahn to chew and an hour went by while mouths moved unceasingly with pahn and chatter.

Suddenly a door burst open and out rushed Zizabai, flushed and triumphant. Dashing into the crowd she sang out, " A girl child! . . . a beautiful girl, like mem-sahib." There were hushed exclamations. " Girl! A girl! Poor Doctor-sahib! A man must have a son to light his funeral pyre, otherwise how can he get into heaven? " It is the son who is valued in India and when he marries his father receives a valuable dowry from the father of the bride. Girl babies are not welcome. Sensing their disappointment, Zizabai burst into a furious torrent of words. " It is good! . . . Good that the Doctor-sahib's mem-sahib has a girl child. The Doctor-sahib is glad! The Christians are right, a girl is as good as a boy! "

Her angry words evoked a great controversial babbling, and the compound bubbled and seethed with the wrangling voices. Victoria May strode out upon the verandah. With tight lips she surveyed the arguing crowd, then burst into a loud command. " Quiet! " Her voice rang through the noisy compound and there was almost instant silence.

" If you wish to brawl," her voice stung, " please take to the streets! " And with a narrow look she disappeared indoors.

Lakshmibai, wife of the village potter, turned aside, her dark eyes welling with tears. She noticed a neighbor, Dayabai, tuck her gift for the new baby into her sari and start toward the gate. A frail widow broke into tears. Slowly the women villagers started sadly out of the courtyard, ashamed at their rude behavior and at Victoria's sharp words. They had disgraced themselves.

And then William appeared on the verandah. He had heard Victoria May's words, knew how they would affect the people, knew that Indians were delicately sensitive, not quick to anger but quickly wounded. It was not difficult for the doctor to summon a smile to his tired face when he thought of the perfect new baby girl and of Mary, now sleeping quietly. His beaming smile picked up the spirits of the people and as his friendly face warmed and reassured them, the atmosphere became charged quite suddenly with festivity and joy. Gifts for the new baby were heaped upon the verandah: fragrant flower garlands, tiny brass drinking vessels, bracelets, anklets and rings for the baby's fingers and toes, tiny sandals, beautiful cloth and toys carved from sandalwood.

As William looked into the smiling faces, faces he had come to know intimately through the sorrows and terrors of plague, the sufferings of their bodies and the comradeship of working together in the warding off of famine, he knew that now these were his people. For all her strange, inscrutable, revolting, endearing, mysterious and terrible ways, he belonged to India, he was part of her people and of their destiny.

" The baby has changed my whole life," Mary told

her husband, but couldn't tell why. " I just can't put
it into words," she apologized. How could she explain her new happiness? I guess it's what they call
" motherhood," thought Mary, although the word had
always sounded drab and duty-laden, while this new
experience carried a glorious sense of joyful responsibility. She stroked the baby's tiny head and
was grateful to the small one for giving her a sense of
direction and fulfillment.

The baby was not as much trouble as Zizabai and
Victoria May, whose constant bickering grew to be
rather a trial. " It is my turn! " Zizabai would pro-
claim loudly the day after Victoria May had aired the
baby in the courtyard. " I am her ayah! " The use
of this term upset Victoria May, for she refused to
apply an Indian word to herself, yet with the possible
exception of the word " mammy " as used in the old
American Confederacy, the English language has no
equivalent for " ayah."

And then she solved her problem. On a bright,
warm morning Victoria May entered the doctor's
bungalow with a gleam in her eye. Facing Mary and
Zizabai she made a triumphant proclamation: " I,"
she began and Mary wanted to smile at her earnestness, " am Ethel's godmother! And as her godmother I insist she be called Ethel and not ' baby '! "
A self-appointed godmother was something new to
Mary, but she merely nodded while Zizabai sulked in
a corner not understanding the awesome title, but
nonplused by its implications.

The season for the Vitoba festival had come. Pilgrims traveling to the great shrine of the god Vitoba in Pandharpur passed in multitudes along the road from Miraj, past the hospital. Caked with dust and sweat, stumbling with weariness, thirst and hunger, on they came, carried forward in a surge of religious ecstasy. Arms were left free for other tasks while heads carried blankets, rice, cooking pots and herbs. The wealthy traveled in litters born by weary servants, others walked or rode upon animals, aged women were stuffed into baskets and carried on the backs of coolies, while ancient blind men groped along the road—all on their way to the festival at the shrine of Vitoba.

Shuffle, shuffle, shuffle. Leather sandals plodded through the dirt of the road. " Bazula za! Bazula za! Hai! Hai! " The drivers of ox-carts and tongas raised their voices in warning as they passed through the plodding, clattering crowd. A weird harmony of sound continued for days on the road through Miraj: the agonized cry of a mother unattended, giving birth to a child; piteous wails of the fallen and exhausted; songs and shouts of encouragement by the strong; wailing babies and fretting children. Glancing out of his window, William saw a woman stumble and fall. She was with her husband and two small children who stopped when she fell. William hurried to assist her. As he approached the road he noticed the man and children leaving this woman on the roadside. " Wait," he called to them. " Perhaps I can help you." He imagined they were going in search of aid. The man, dressed in a dirty white dhoti, cast a curious glance at William.

" Your wife? " William indicated the ominously still figure on the roadside.

The man nodded, frowned.

" Is she sick? If so I'll be glad to take care of her."

But the native shook his dusty, turbaned head. " She is dead," he announced in a flat, emotionless voice.

Then William looked at the little family. The children had divided the mother's household effects between them and it was obvious that the three intended to continue their journey without a pause.

" But you can't leave her like this," the doctor argued, while he tried to understand their callousness in the face of death. A wife and mother, doubtless devoted to her family, left in death like an animal.

The native showed signs of impatience. He gestured in the direction of his dead wife. " She is dead. It is the will of God." And with the fateful shrug of his shoulders he started down the road. He and his sons could not waste time. They were on their way to the festival.

As William looked at the dead woman he noticed her work-ridged hands, her tired, patient face. She had given her life in service to her husband and he let her drop by the wayside like a withered leaf drops from a tree.

" If the meek shall inherit the earth," William said later to Mary, " a large percentage of the population will be Indian wives."

The next morning in his consulting room at the hospital, surrounded by an ever-increasing number of people, William patiently and efficiently checked over each new arrival. As he applied a stethoscope to a suspected tubercular chest, he became aware of the entrance of one of the pilgrims who had fallen out of the procession and staggered into the hospital for help. William looked at him sharply. The man had evidently come far. Perhaps from the Punjab region, for his complexion was fairer than the Hindus of the south.

Then suddenly the man collapsed. His wasted body shook and heaved. He clutched his stomach. As William dashed to his side the man started to vomit a peculiar, rice-water-like fluid. William clenched his teeth. This symptom was peculiar to one disease—cholera.

The doctor gestured to the other patients in the room. " Out! Out! " he ordered. They left quickly, curiosity written on their faces.

Within a few days there were others with the same nauseating symptoms.

" They've picked this up somewhere along the way," complained the doctor, " and what's worse, they've probably left the germs for others." He thought of the case of one cholera victim who so contaminated a village drinking pool that one thousand villagers died of the same disease.

"Who knows how many drinking pools these people have used on their way to the festival?" William shook his head sadly. Sometimes the sanitation problem appeared too overwhelming for solution.

"Segregate these people," William ordered. "Disinfect all the drinking tanks and wells but don't let the villagers hear of it. There's no need for useless fear."

But the villagers did hear of it. Like a quiet trickle of poison the word went through the village.

"Muree Ai is angry."

"We have displeased Muree Ai."

"Muree Ai, Muree Ai."

Lakshmibai, the potter's wife, hurried into the courtyard of her neighbor. Dayabai was busy weaving. "Muree Ai is displeased," whispered Lakshmibai fearfully as her thin hand clutched the glass beads about her throat. "Muree Ai is angry. We must take offerings at once to Muree Ai."

The neighbor took her foot from the treadle, laid down the green and gold-wrapped shuttles. "Muree Ai?" She glanced with anxious eyes toward the verandah where two sturdy, naked children laughed and played. "We must appease Muree Ai," she told Lakshmibai, but the potter's wife made another suggestion. "Why not trust the Doctor-sahib?" she asked. "He drove the famine from the village. He cared for us during the plague." Her voice faltered at the indignation in her neighbor's face.

" Would you have us all die? " the woman whispered hoarsely. " You know Muree Ai becomes angry if we take medicine. She would vent her wrath upon the entire village if one of us went to the Doctor-sahib. For famine, yes. For plague, yes. But for cholera . . . no! Muree Ai is the Goddess of Cholera and she must be appeased. Otherwise we shall all die. We had better do as Muree Ai demands."

" We must appease Muree Ai . . . appease Muree Ai . . ." Word spread through the village. The wayside shrine of Mother Cholera, filled with shape-less rocks painted red, suddenly became the center of fervent and worshipful attention. " Muree Ai, we implore you do not become angry with your chil-dren." " Here, here are gifts for you, Muree Ai." Before the reddened stones heaps of gifts grew into mounds. Eggs, rice, sweetmeats and yards of green cloth. Green was the favorite color of Muree Ai. " What is the Mother's pleasure? " " Tell us." But Muree Ai was evidently unhappy for more cases of cholera developed in the village. The people be-came frightened.

William's reassuring voice rang out. " Don't be afraid. Follow the simple health rules I have taught you. Keep your drinking tanks clean and don't let the oxen wallow in them. Above all—eat no fruit which has not been thoroughly washed! " But Wil-liam sensed their panic; knew they were afraid of

the wrath of the goddess and completely unconcerned
about the condition of their drinking tanks. "Wash
the fruit! Wash it!" But he knew from their eyes
that they were afraid only of Muree Ai, of the ancient
laws and legends. He treated the sick while the well
hurried to appease their angry goddess.

As she brought early-morning food to a maternity
patient, Zizabai heard excited voices and the whining
wheels of a cart upon the Miraj road. Running to
the window she looked into the new morning, then
snorted with disgust. Through the dust she could not
see details, but Zizabai recognized on the dry road a
procession and remembered others in which she had
walked. The mass of villagers surrounded a crude
cart and she knew that in that (four-wheeled) cart
was a tiny statue of Muree Ai. Mother Cholera,
accompanied by her regretful worshippers, was being
taken to another village. The murmuring voices
blurred through the stifling dust and Zizabai knew
what they were saying. "We regret your departure,
dear Muree Ai." "It grieves our hearts that you
cannot stay longer with us." "We envy those to
whom you go, dear mother." "We shall miss you,
Muree Ai." And all the while they were hoping
desperately that the dreaded old Muree Ai would not
trouble them again for many years.

Zizabai's wrath was so intense that she did not
hear Victoria May until the older woman stood beside her.

" Why are you wasting time staring out of that window? You ought to be at work! "

Furious black eyes snapped at her and Victoria May experienced a momentary shock. " Fools! " Zizabai snorted.

" What? " Victoria May's voice ran the scale.

" Those out there! " Zizabai pointed toward the disappearing procession. " They smile, double up their stomachs with bowing when they take Muree Ai away. They say ' too bad ' and ' we miss you,' but in their hearts they say ' you bad old woman, you stay away from us!' Fools! " repeated Zizabai vehemently.

Victoria May looked curiously at the small, indignant figure. " Why do you call your own people fools? "

Zizabai thrust out her well-developed chin. " Everybody fool who believes different than white doctor's mem-sahib," she declared staunchly, her loyalty to Mary having overcome her inborn prejudices and superstitions.

" Then why don't you become a Christian? " Victoria May asked for the one hundredth time. She was very much annoyed by Zizabai. It was ridiculous. This little heathen relinquished with abandon her own beliefs, but steadfastly refused to accept Christianity. Victoria May's well-developed conscience twinged regularly because the girl was neither one thing nor the other. " The doctor's mem-sahib is a firm and devoted Christian," she added

Zizabai knelt by Mary and offered her basket.

with a triumphant nod, knowing this argument carried weight with Zizabai.

Zizabai clenched her teeth, her nostrils flared. "Fool!" This time she spoke directly at Victoria May. The word hissed into the startled morning like a serpent.

After Victoria May's blood pressure returned to normal, she turned from the window. "Control, Victoria, control!" And with a firm grip upon her temper she went back to work.

"Mem-sahib, I bring you something."

To Mary, fanning herself and the baby with a *punkah,* the voice was as welcome as a cool drink. With a smile she greeted the entrance of Zizabai into the hot bungalow. Zizabai frowned with concern at the doctor's mem-sahib. She was so thin since the coming of the baby. Her cheeks were not pink and her lips were pale.

"Here, mem-sahib."

The tiny, dark figure knelt by Mary and offered a basket. She had hurried to the bazaar early in the morning when she might obtain the finest, most luscious fruits for her beloved mem-sahib.

"How good they look!" Mary exclaimed enjoying the bold colors of yellow plantains, the bright-gold oranges and the plump, purple grapes. "I haven't had grapes for so long," Mary remarked hungrily.

The baby fretted in her basket. Zizabai rushed to

her side and with a melting glance asked, " Mem-sahib, please may I sit with missy-baba on the verandah? "

" Of course," Mary answered, and smiled as the eager girl gathered up the pink and white baby mur-muring, " Now, your ayah she takes care of you. Come with ayah, missy-baba. Good missy-baba." The baby's fretting ceased as the devoted Zizabai took her onto the verandah. Mary sat at their small writing desk and started a letter to her father in Toronto.

" Dear Papa," she began. What could she tell him? No use to mention the heat, he'd only worry. Mary nibbled at the end of her pen, then looked at the basket of fruit. Those plantains looked good. But no, they were so filling. Oh, she'd forgotten to send pictures of the baby in her last letter. " I am sending pictures of Ethel for sure in this letter. As you can see she is in excellent health and my world simply moves around her. William is so busy at the hospital." Mary pecked thoughtfully at the pen once more, then reached out for a grape. How re-freshing, she thought as she ground it between her teeth, then continued writing. " He has more pa-tients than he can attend to. I'm afraid he is over-working though he claims he is feeling fine. If he only had some assistants. Victoria May Hastings, Zizabai and I do most of the nursing, though since the baby came I only work in the surgical. We have a few native helpers, but we could use many more.

Sick people come from all over India for care from William's hands and his operations are miracles." Mary glanced down at the basket of fruit. She'd eaten a whole cluster of grapes. She must save some for William. Suddenly Mary remembered. She hadn't washed them.

" Zizabai," she called, " did you wash those grapes? "

" Oh! " Zizabai's voice was a pang of regret. Her anxious figure appeared in the doorway.

" Never mind." Mary managed a smile.

" Mem-sahib did not eat them yet? "

Mary smiled reassuringly. " How foolish," she remarked lightly.

Zizabai smiled with relief and turned back to the baby.

Mary stood irresolute. Should I tell William, she thought. But from the bungalow she could see the long line of weary, hot sufferers waiting to see the doctor. No use to become alarmed. She felt all right. There wasn't one chance in a thousand that the grapes were contaminated. Casting the thought from her mind she turned back to her letter.

That afternoon was one of William's busiest. The small operating theatre became the scene of one major operation after another. Mary and Victoria May relieved each other as the skilled hands of the surgeon never seemed to tire. Hour after hour . . . operation after operation. The removal of a great tumor, amputation of a gangrenous leg, extraction of cataracts, Caesarian delivery of a set of twins, the delicate removal of a goitre . . . Mary's brain swam when she attempted to recall the rest.

It was well after dark when William returned to the bungalow for dinner and a comforting chat with his wife.

" Mary," he announced as they sat before an open window hoping for a stray breeze, " you need a vacation. How would you like to take a trip? "

Mary glanced at him in amazement. " Could you go with me? "

" Of course." His eyes held a secret.

" But the hospital? "

" We'll manage somehow," he said. " After all, we're entitled to a vacation by this time."

" Oh, William! " She looked into his eyes joyfully.

" I was wondering," he paused searching her eager face, " if you would like to see the Taj Mahal."

Try as she might, Mary couldn't keep the tears from her eyes. The Taj Mahal—at last. But a troubling thought came. " What about the baby? "

" It will take about a month to make our arrangements so by that time the baby should be able to travel in complete safety."

The quick rush of color into Mary's cheeks and her sparkling eyes lifted William's weariness, and they spent the evening making eager plans.

It was eleven o'clock when the doctor picked up

his lantern and started for the door. He must make his last rounds of the day and look in on the most serious operation cases.

" William," Mary joined him at the door, a basket of washed fruit in her hand, " let me go with you."

" Good! Come along."

As they trudged through the compound watching their lantern-lit path for snakes, the doctor joked: " Did you bring that fruit for me? "

" No," she shook her head. " It's for that missionary patient who came in yesterday. She said if she didn't have some fresh fruit to eat that she was going to give up. So . . ." Her voice trailed off in a soft laugh.

The doctor tucked his arm through hers and murmured, " Always thinking of someone else. You're a good girl, Mary. A good girl." And he was glad that she was finally going to see the Taj Mahal.

After they had gone to bed, Mary tossed restlessly. Pictures she had seen of the fairyland Taj Mahal kaleidoscoped in her mind. White, glittering marble, silvered pools and delicate, inlaid mother-of-pearl formed ceaseless patterns. She tried to lie still and not disturb William. He was so tired. And tomorrow there would be more and more operations.

Suddenly she felt chilled. That was strange. She touched her face. It was wet. Perspiration poured from her forehead. That's what excitement did. She must try and forget about the Taj. Try and sleep. The grapes! Those unwashed grapes! Mary tried to fight down her rising fear. There was nothing the matter with her, nothing. She turned toward William. He was sleeping the sleep of one exhausted. Tomorrow there would be so many operations. The thing to do was to go to sleep. The morning would be the same as any other morning. She'd get up. They would have chota hazri. She would feed the baby . . . feed the baby . . . Mary winced. A pain attacked her stomach. Think about the morning . . . the blessed daylight. There was comfort in ordinary things. The dressing of the baby . . . the rounds of the wards where grateful faces watched eagerly for the nurses and the beloved Doctor-sahib. There would be luncheon at noon, and William would take his fifteen-minute rest. Then . . . But the pain again. Mary gritted her teeth. She would not cry out. This was ridiculous. It was excitement. Only excitement over seeing the Taj. The beautiful Taj. Mary felt the perspiration break out anew on her face, then over her body. Nighttime magnified everything so. She must sleep . . . sleep. But the night hours lagged. " Come, morning, come, morning," begged Mary.

How still the hospital yard was in the moonlight. The jacaranda tree she'd planted cast fringed shadows over the verandah. Soon there would be purple blossoms. That pain again! She must have cried out for William stirred.

" What's the matter, Mary? " he asked sleepily.

"I—I don't feel well," she answered.

With the quick response of doctors William became instantly alert. "What is it?" His voice was quick, calm.

Mary hated herself for awakening him but she felt so much worse. "My head. I feel cold and yet I'm perspiring. I think I'm going to be sick at my stomach!"

William leaped from the bed, quickly tended to her needs. Instantly he knew the trouble. There was not a second to be lost.

"Sitabai!"

The gentle serving-woman responded at once.

"Bring Victoria May here," he told her as the little woman stared with horror at Mary and into the Doctor-sahib's face, inscrutable in the glow of the lamp.

The hospital yard and bungalows were quiet, but there was little sleep. Anxiety pries into sleep and soon not only Victoria May and Zizabai were awake but patients lying in wards caught the sense of trouble and fretted and tossed in their sleep.

"Brandy," directed William. "She must be stimulated. A hypodermic! Heat applications!"

Victoria May, grim and white-faced, obeyed every order with the promptness of an automaton. Zizabai was completely useless. Crouching outside the bedroom door she slowly tore her sari into shreds as her nervous fingers clutched for support. Whom could she call upon? Not her old gods . . . yet not the new Christian God whom she did not know. There was no one. And Zizabai choked with bitter sobs as the Doctor-sahib worked feverishly in the lamplight, his face like a mask.

For hours the only noise in the bungalow was the curt, crisp orders given by William, and the quick " yes " of Victoria May to every command. There was no hesitation, no indecision. William did everything in his power. There was but one difficulty. Mary had called so late.

But William didn't dare think. With the objective calm of a scientist, with every ounce of his strength and all the wisdom at his command he worked efficiently, quickly, skilfully.

The terrible early hours brought no improvement. The muscle in William's cheek worked now . . . still his face was calm . . . his hands sure. He felt the pulse. It was slow and heavy; tired with life. William's clothes dripped with perspiration. The arteries on his forehead stood out like fiercely-enclosed rivers. He was fighting, fighting with everything in him against the slowly-encircling shadow.

" Oh, God," he breathed. " God help me." Closer now came the dread shadow . . . William pitted himself against it.

" Mary . . . Mary, don't give up! Fight, Mary, fight! "

But the heavy lids fluttered over the beautiful grey eyes. She was tired . . . tired . . .

And then—it was over. A quick, mocking second

before there had been life. Now there was none. William stood motionless, his skilful hands hung vanquished. It was Victoria May who pulled the sheet up over the lovely face, while the sound of Zizabai's wails were like the lonely jackal's in the night.

IT WAS three weeks since Mary's death. Victoria May watched the doctor anxiously as he opened his morning mail. A grim despair had fastened itself upon his face. "If only he'd break out of his shell," the maiden lady muttered to herself. "Get angry, or lose his temper or something. Anything would be better than this awful silence." But she knew that William carried his hurt deep and would share it with no one.

"Victoria May!"

His voice caused her to jump. It was the first time in three weeks that he had spoken with a trace of enthusiasm. As she faced him over his desk, he was reading from a letter.

"Look at this." His haggard eyes brightened, a faint smile touched his lips. "We're going to have more help. A nurse."

"Well!" She set her shoulders. "It's high time!" She scurried to his side, looked at the letter. "What are the details? When is she coming? What's her name?"

"She'll be here on the twentieth," he said. "Five more days."

"That's answer to prayer if I ever heard of one." Victoria May drew up a chair beside the desk. Then she leaned forward and spoke seriously. "William,

I want to have a little talk with you." He glanced at his watch. " It will only take a second," she insisted, " and it's important."

" All right." He leaned back with a heavy sigh. " But I must be at the dispensary in ten minutes."

" It's about this nursing business," she plunged right to the point. He nodded. " William, I know I'm not capable enough to continue as head nurse. I've done my best these past three weeks," she explained, " but I was never prepared for the work like Mary was." She paused, bit her lip. " So when the new nurse comes . . . By the way, what's her name ? "

He glanced at the letter. " Mildred Mumford."

She sniffed. " American ? "

" Milwaukee, Wisconsin."

" Well, when this Mildred Mumford comes, I want her to take the job of head nurse. What little knowledge of nursing I have I learned from Mary. And if it hadn't been for her patience . . ." she faltered, tears welling in her eyes.

William leaned forward, touched her hand gently.

" I understand," he said and then stood up. " If you'll take charge of our Indian nurses," he suggested, " Miss Mumford can take care of the other work."

Victoria May wiped her eyes, then continued. " There's one more thing," she said. " It's about Zizabai."

" Yes ? " William wondered if the youthful widow

could be ill. He recalled that he hadn't seen her around the compound for some days.

" She's gone."

" Gone? You mean she's run away? "

Victoria May nodded. " She grieved so about Mary. I never saw anyone take on so in all my life. I guess she thought she was responsible—those grapes and all. But just a week ago she disappeared. Nobody has the least idea where she went."

William was silent a moment. " Who's been caring for the baby? "

" One of the native nurses has been taking care of her," she explained. " I would have told you this sooner—but, well, I knew you had enough on your mind."

William made no comment, but walked toward the door. When Mary was taken his whole world had tumbled. For days life had had no meaning . . . but he went his rounds, tended to the sick and performed operations with a dogged persistence. Too discouraged to ask, too tired to pray, too heartsick to hope, he had clung desperately to the belief that beyond his sorrow and tragedy there was a Plan, and he was part of it. He felt no emotional reaction to Zizabai's disappearance—only another small burden upon his already overburdened shoulders. He thought about the letter. A nurse was on her way. Things were going forward. Into his mind flashed something of the Plan. " I am to dedicate myself to this hospital, body and soul. I shall give it my every thought. This is my life.'' Grasping this idea with strength born of despair, William plunged into the hospital routine, working from earliest morning until late, late at night.

There was quite a stir through the hospital the morning Miss Mumford was to arrive. As William watched Victoria May clatter down the road in her ancient *bandi* he tried not to remember that it was the same conveyance which several years before had carried Mary and him up the dusty road from Sangli station to their Indian adventure. '' Miss Mumford. Mildred Mumford,'' he repeated to himself as the name brought up visions of a plump, capable trained nurse.

One half hour later, as the *bandi* jogged into the hospital compound, William thought he had been clairvoyant. Seated beside Victoria May, Miss Mumford looked exactly as he had visualized her. Plump, brown-haired, youthful and vigorous. William approached, a feeling of satisfaction welling in his heart. It was while Victoria May performed introductions that he noticed with a shock that Miss Mumford's eyes were red. She had been crying.

'' Miss Mumford,'' Victoria May's face was expressionless, '' this is our Dr. Wanless. Dr. Wanless, your new head nurse.''

As William held out his hand, Miss Mumford clasped it loosely. '' How do you do? '' she managed while she stared at his face, then tears filled her eyes.

"Oh, Dr. Wanless, I hope you'll excuse me for acting this way . . ." She struggled for control, then finally blurted out, "I miss my Alfred!"

"Your husband?" William's voice was expressionless.

Miss Mumford colored. "Gracious, no. Alfred's my beau . . . he was steady, too, until . . . until . . ." here she gurgled again while she fought to hold back her tears, "we had a spat!"

William felt ten years older. He had hoped so desperately for a head nurse. But this young woman was far too emotional. As he turned away some of his disappointment must have registered in his attitude, for Miss Mumford hurried after him, pulled at his sleeve.

"You're disappointed in me, aren't you, Dr. Wanless? But you needn't be." A kind of desperation seized her. "I'll nurse the sick and do just what you tell me. And even though my heart's breaking—I'll work so hard that maybe I'll work myself to death!" Hope glimmered in her watery blue eyes as she announced melodramatically, "Maybe if I *do* die, Alfred will be sorry!" The prospect of a conscience-smitten Alfred prostrated at her bier so cheered her that she brightened up and hurried into the hospital.

William watched her broad figure disappear into the building. He clenched his hands, thrust them deep into his pockets and muttered, "Lord, how much more? How much more?" then went to prepare for the afternoon's operations.

Mildred Mumford proved to be a fairly capable nurse when her mind was on her business. She got along well with the Indian people, accepting their customs without comment. One afternoon, after a particularly helpful performance in the operating room, William had a faint hope that she might develop into a satisfactory head nurse. His hopes were cut short, however, when Miss Mumford approached him with a letter.

" From my chum in Milwaukee," she confided. " She's been watching Alfred for me, and she writes that he's pining! " She giggled. " Pining away to a splinter, so Effie says here."

" Very interesting," drily observed the doctor. " May I ask if this news had anything to do with your excellent performance in the operating room today? "

Miss Mumford faced him squarely. " Oh, yes! " she admitted. " When I know that Alfred misses me, there's nothing I can't do! " She passed her letter to the doctor.

" There's something in here that you'll be interested in." She paused. " My chum, Effie Pfieffer— the one who wrote the letter—is coming to India to be a nurse."

William pricked up his ears. Another nurse. Hope held out a flickering candle which was blown out by Miss Mumford's words.

" Effie's a nurse—just like I am! "

Not too much like you, hoped the doctor, as he scanned Miss Pfieffer's letter and learned that, " I'm coming to India just as soon as I can throw my clothes into a half-dozen suitcases and two trunks.''

Responsibility for the care of Baby Ethel rested heavily upon Victoria May. Because of Miss Mumford's whimsicality it was necessary for the older woman to spend most of her time at the hospital, leaving Ethel in the hands of an Indian woman who was not too well-schooled in the care of a white baby.

'' I really didn't appreciate Zizabai,'' lamented Victoria May as she recalled the youthful widow's love for the '' missy-baba,'' and her gentle care.

And then, as suddenly as she had disappeared, just that suddenly Zizabai returned.

Victoria May, busy feeding Ethel, looked up from the baby and there in the doorway stood Zizabai, as if she had never been away.

'' I have come back,'' said the girl simply. '' I want to follow the Jesus-way.''

And with as little effort as she uttered her words, did the lovely native girl turn to her new way of life. Her every word and action were in strict accord with the commandments of her new God.

'' Zizabai,'' the older woman called the girl to her one morning.

'' Yes, Missi-sahib.''

How different she looks, thought Victoria May, without her heathenish array of jewelry. Different— and beautiful. The grey-haired woman tried to appear stern.

" I have a new duty for you, young lady," she said, hoping her eyes wouldn't give away the secret.

But Zizabai's voice had become happily obedient. " Any duty you say," she answered with a smile.

" Zizabai," Victoria May looked deep into the pretty face before you, " I want you to take complete charge of Ethel, the—er—missy-baba as you call her."

Zizabai's eyes flashed wide open, followed by a sweep of joy across her face. " I am to be the missy-baba's ayah? " She spoke as if her hearing had deceived her.

Victoria May nodded. " You will be her ayah," she said and from the ecstasy on the face of the new convert knew that no child would ever have a more loving, devoted ayah than Zizabai.

" She's coming today! Effie's coming today! " sang out Mildred Mumford as she rubbed a bit of flour on her face to take off the shine.

William went about his work methodically, anxiously awaiting the arrival of his new nurse. The Effie Pfieffer would *have* to be the right one. He *had* to be relieved of some of the responsibility. As a tonga clattered into the compound he strained to catch a glimpse of her. Shaking his head the doctor looked again. Besides Victoria May and a young woman, there was also a man in the tonga. A thought cut across William's mind. Could this be Alfred come to claim Mildred? He fervently hoped so. They could be married at the hospital, she could continue on as nurse and Alfred might be trained as a compounder. He could use a good English-speaking man. And then the doctor smiled at the eagerness of his brain and went out to welcome the new nurse.

" Effie! Effie! " Mildred was smothering her friend in a close embrace.

At that moment all that could be seen of Effie was a great picture hat with massive plumes. As Mildred released her hold upon her Milwaukee friend, William was treated to his first glimpse of Effie Pfieffer. It was difficult to find the girl behind the clothes. Dressed in the height of fashion, her blond hair brushed into a high pompadour, she was almost obscured by leg-o'-mutton sleeves, a draped, ruffled skirt, a lacy umbrella, gloves, boa and a pocketbook.

" Don't judge by appearances . . . not by appearances," William told himself as Mildred introduced the new arrival. As he acknowledged the introduction William glanced curiously toward the young Englishman standing in the background. Effie followed his glance, then blushed and dimpled. " This is Cecil," she tittered fondly. The doctor shook hands wondering who in the world Cecil might be.

" I say—jolly glad to meet you! " Cecil toyed with his walking stick, then turned to Effie. " Don't you think we'd better tell the doctor? "

He was stopped by a quick glance. " Not yet! " Effie tossed her plumed hat, then smiled charmingly at William. " Cecil has to be in Calcutta next week, so you don't mind if he stays here for a day or two, do you? "

" Oh, I say," Cecil protested, uneasy under William's searching gaze. As Effie fluttered away, tittering with Mildred Mumford, the Englishman added lamely, " Beastly hot weather, hey? " William nodded, while his heart sank. Without ever seeing Effie Pfieffer engaged in hospital routine, something told him she was not cut out for a nurse.

Late that evening a knock sounded on the door of the doctor's bungalow. Opening it, he discovered Miss Mumford and Miss Pfieffer clinging together, eyeing him beseechingly.

" Well, ladies? " He had seated them, closed the door, and now came directly to the point. Miss Pfieffer looked at Miss Mumford and giggled. Miss Mumford looked at Miss Pfieffer and giggled also.

William felt a rush of impatience. " If there's anything I can do for you . . ."

Miss Pfieffer answered impulsively, " There is! You can marry us! "

" What? " He glanced from Miss Pfieffer to Miss Mumford. Miss Mumford explained.

" It's Effie and Cecil," she sighed romantically.

" Yes," substantiated Miss Pfieffer, " it's Cecil and I."

" They want to be married." Miss Mumford beamed at her friend.

Miss Pfieffer blushed. " You see, he has an appointment in Calcutta. Fine pay and all—and he wants me to go there with him as his wife." She glanced at Miss Mumford and they both tittered.

William sighed heavily. " Didn't you come to India as a nurse, Miss Pfieffer? " he asked.

She looked crestfallen. " But I've had a proposal."

" So I understand." The doctor leaned back in his chair. " When did you meet this young man? "

" Cecil? " Her eyes grew big. " Ever since he got on the boat at Liverpool." She clasped her hands together. " It was on the deck we first met. He was going one way and I ——"

" Effie! " Mildred Mumford sensed the doctor's impatience. " He didn't ask how. Just when."

" Oh." Effie smiled. " When he boarded at Liverpool." She leaned toward William winningly. " Dr. Wanless, Cecil and I want to be married right away. And I was wondering . . ." She twisted her lace handkerchief. " Well, inasmuch as my father isn't here or anything—would you be willing to give me away? "

William dropped his face into his hands. If the implications were not so serious it would have been funny. His new nurse—his hope for help—and she wanted him to give her away in marriage so she could leave. Well, why not? Straightening up the doctor surprised even himself by the ring in his voice.

" Be glad to! " he answered and Effie wondered if perhaps he was glad to be rid of her.

Victoria May was busy training Indian girls, but so few had the slightest education or elementary knowledge of hygiene. Most had to be schooled in both their own language and English before attempting to start on nursing work. As the months rolled by William merely gritted his teeth, sent pleading letters to America and Canada for more nurses, and did about ten men's work by himself.

In answer to his urgent letters to churches at home, more nurses arrived, but for many, nursing was only an interlude between romantic dreams and marriage. They marked time with bandaging, feeding, and changing beds while they eagerly searched every available white male face as a possible release from the burden of spinsterhood. They had hoped that on shipboard perhaps, or on their way to the mission station, that there might come "that one." They were seldom disappointed. The daily mail at Miraj hospital dripped with sugared missiles from one stricken young man or another, and as time went on these young women were claimed in marriage by rapt young men who never dreamed that their shy little brides were as intrepid as the most daring jungle hunters in stalking their game.

The victories of these triumphant ones meant misery for William. He had to have nurses. He had yet to find a satisfactory head nurse.

"I'm Emma Harries."
William looked up one morning in his office to find

the owner of the low, hollow voice. He had been notified of the coming of a new nurse, but because of previous disappointments paid little attention. But there was something about this voice. He glanced up hopefully. The moment his eyes rested upon her he knew she was the one—his new head nurse. Tall, raw-boned, tight-lipped, but capable to the tips of her big, flat fingers—Emma Harries was the answer. With no fuss or bother she entered into the hospital routine as if she had been born and trained in Miraj.

One afternoon as she was preparing to enter the operating room, Emma Harries found herself face to face with the most startling man she had ever seen. Simply dressed, he loomed in the doorway, three hundred and fifty pounds of Hindu gentleman. He salaamed.

" I should like to watch Dr. Wanless in the operating room."

Emma Harries gasped, then realized that perhaps this was a friend of the doctor's.

" Well . . ." she hesitated.

" I have been admitted before," he said helpfully and moved toward the operating theatre.

" Oh, no, you don't! " cried Emma running after him. " You don't set foot in there without a cap and gown for antiseptic reasons! " And hurrying to a cupboard she brought out the necessary articles and thrust them upon him.

As William donned his mask, he sensed the pres-

ence of someone in the doorway and glanced up. He
stared. Suddenly the bleak grimness of past months
dissolved into rejuvenating laughter. There stood
the huge Maharajah, three hundred and fifty pounds
of him, trying to wear a regulation cap and gown.
William howled with laughter. On the monarch's
expansive frontal area the usually ample gown looked
like a small, silly apron, while he had removed the
royal turban and was trying valiantly to balance the
stiff, white cap upon his great head. He knew he
looked ridiculous for he, himself, was rocking with
laughter. When Emma rushed into the room to dis-
cover the cause of such hilarity she found the two
men, tears of laughter running down their faces,
gasping and leaning on the operating table for support.

Within the next week, Emma Harries had fashioned with her own hands a massive, white robe and
cap which were the exclusive property of the Maharajah of Kolhapur to be worn whenever he came to be
an observing guest in the operating room. After that
day he came often, for the complex and breath-taking
operations performed by his doctor friend were a
source of endless wonder and delight to him.

The lack of caste observance at Miraj hospital continued to be of prime importance to the Maharajah.
To one brought up under the rigid caste system, the
doctor's demand for equality took on the aura of a
miracle.

At Miraj men learned to their surprise and gratification that they were not too different one from the other. Those of a high caste found themselves experiencing the same fears, pains and triumphs as the lowest blind beggar, when, after a cataract removal, they found themselves able to see the world about them. The oneness of suffering and of recovery bound together those who came under the skilful care of the wonder-working doctor of Miraj.

"Wanless" and "Miraj" had grown to mean magic of India. From Ceylon to the Himalayas; from Persia, Afghanistan and South Africa came sick and suffering, hearing of the healing doctor. They called him "Miracle Doctor," "The Wizard of India." Wealthy Parsees from Bombay again and again expressed their gratitude with gifts of money and William built more and more wards, bungalows and cottages for the hospital. But never did he have enough help.

His shoulders grew stooped. His step was tired. But on he went, day after day, with a bulldog tenacity.

"One of these days you'll find out you've been working too hard," cautioned the worried Victoria May, "and then you'll be sorry!"

But William turned from her advice and continued to give himself completely to the work. Through his mind raced the words . . . "So much to be done . . . so much to be done."

13

As THE early sunlight brightened his bungalow, William found himself unable to move from bed. He groaned and thought of Victoria May's warning: "You'll work too hard . . . you'll work too hard."

It had seemed ridiculous, this warning about "working too hard" when energy poured from his finger tips and each onward-marching moment held a challenge, an unexpected urgency. Even now, before the day's vast influx of new sufferers for diagnosis and treatment, the greater part of today's work had already been scheduled: a heavy tumor to be removed from an old man's shoulder, a delicate operation for gallstones on a woman, intestinal worms to be removed from a boy of six, the almost daily cataract operations, a probably Caesarian-section delivery for a pitiful child-wife, and a skin grafting operation for a woman who had been severely burned when her sari attracted quick flames from an open cooking place. These and other operations besides the daily round of all wards and the never-ending number of problems intruding upon the day's tight routine.

"I haven't time to be sick," William moaned through a drawn mouth while his teeth chattered like an Indian rattle.

There was little doubt in his mind as to the trouble.

For a week now, Indians suffering with dengue-malaria fever had appeared at the hospital. He had segregated them, taking every precaution. Now his symptoms were the same. First the tired, weary feeling, then nausea, next the beginning of the chill and after ten minutes or more the hot stage when the perspiration starts.

Sitabai, preparing breakfast, became aware of strange mutterings from the Doctor-sahib's room. She listened. His voice again. Perhaps he was calling to her. She hurried to the door, rapped gently. The voice continued. It sounded incoherent. Softly she opened the door and looked in. As she did so her eyes grew big, a gasp came from her open lips. The strong, active Doctor-sahib lay in his bed and it was apparent even to Sitabai that he was a sick man. Moving as quickly as her sari and native sandals would permit, the frightened woman summoned Victoria May.

" I knew it! " Victoria May's lips were grim. " Working day and night with never a moment's rest." Donning a cape she sped to the bungalow, followed by a worried Sitabai.

As they entered the room and Victoria May took a look at William, she snorted, " I told you so! "

" Dengue-malaria," announced William, steeling himself against any quibbling. " Quinine! " he directed, while his tongue grew thick. " Get me some quinine and——"

" I'll take care of this! " Victoria May turned to

Sitabai. " Go get Emma Harries," she ordered, then fastened her attention upon the sick doctor. Her mind was deeply troubled. With William bedridden who was to do his work? hold the clinic? perform the operations? superintend the overcrowded hospital? Emma Harries was too new to take charge of other than nursing work. But the most important question of all spun round and round in Victoria May's mind, causing her to feel giddy. Would she and Miss Harris be able to nurse William through this illness? How she wished there was a doctor to take responsibility. He was run down, he had sadly overworked, and now to be attacked by this tropical disease! The severe face grew troubled. The tremendous responsibility for the life of this man, so important to India, shook her.

" I never knew what it meant to be directly responsible for life," Victoria May told herself over and over again. " And now to be responsible for him, of all people! "

Zizabai offered not even an ear for solace. The lovely young native ayah jealously guarded the toddling baby in her bungalow, fearful that the dreaded dengue-malaria would reach out and strike her " missy-baba." Under Emma Harries' direction the few Indian nurses made early-morning rounds, doing what they could to relieve the patients, but the situation was impossible from Victoria May's point of view. " We must have another doctor. He must come here immediately! " The words were like an ultimatum though she delivered them only to the gentle, troubled Sitabai.

Each sickening time the thought of William's possible death came to her, Victoria May's heart grew limp. Miraj without Dr. Wanless would be like a desert. He was the guiding beam, he was the pivot around which all the healings took place. He was Miraj—and that was a mistake. Of course it was a mistake! Even as she tended him in her most anxious moments, her heart grew less troubled with the solution to the whole problem. The work was too big for one man. William must have helpers—even if he had to train them himself. An eagerness shook the starched figure. By training other doctors William could multiply himself and his efforts. Two or three hours a day given to the training of new men would mean additional help. Internes at the beginning— later full-fledged doctors.

But first, before anything else, William must be made well.

The day John Holmes made his appearance Victoria May had faltered into the hospital, red-eyed from an all-night vigil at the doctor's bedside and moaned to the head nurse, " I feel about as cheerful as something crawling around in the bottom of a well." Smothered under heavy responsibilities, she only glanced with impatience at the nondescript young white man standing hesitantly inside the compound with a suitcase in his hand.

" If he's some globe-trotter who expects a lot of

entertaining and thinks I'm going to spend time showing him around," she snapped, " he's badly mistaken! "

It was not until the young man had reached the door and timidly repeated his name that Victoria May's face took on the look of one witnessing a miracle.

" I'm Dr. John Holmes," he repeated and cleared his throat conscientiously.

" Doctor? " she gasped, and suddenly his colorless hair and common face were transformed. To Victoria May he was a shining knight, a rescuer who glowed with glory and had dashed to her aid when all seemed lost. Her dilated eyes caused him a twinge of uneasiness. " I—er ——" John hesitated. " I— I came to see Dr. Wanless. Is he not expecting an assistant? " He tried to force a smile but his embarrassment swallowed it and only a sickly grin remained. " The Board sent out an appeal for doctors, and I—I . . ." She continued to stare, and John's voice faltered. " But—but—if you think he doesn't need me . . ."

" Need you? " she cried out so loudly that he jumped. " Young man, you're an angel straight out of heaven! "

Even in his secretly modest dreams, John could not have conceived of the enthusiasm with which he was welcomed at Miraj. He not only felt welcomed but actually snatched into the life of the hospital. Expecting to serve a humble but helpful apprenticeship under the great Dr. Wanless, John amazingly discovered himself bundled into a white hospital-gown and given full responsibility for the recovery of this man whose fame had reached even into the depths of Nova Scotia and into John's heart.

" If I'd only known that you were coming," Victoria May said, breathing more easily now, " it would have saved me so much worry."

She soon discovered that the Board had sent a letter announcing his arrival, but, unfortunately, the letter had failed to reach Miraj before he did. Later, she learned that all through his four years' course of medical study, he had dreamed of going to Miraj. " Some day I'm going to be a medical missionary like Dr. Wanless," he would say, showing his friends clippings from newspapers, which told of the doctor's marvelous achievements in India.

He remembered the baleful scoffing of his one living relative. " If Aunt Sophie could only see me now," he said, assuming his new responsibilities.

John shuddered at his own inadequacies, yet went to work with quiet determination, for the doctor's fever was higher, the malaria gripping its victim with rigid hands.

" No, Kali, no! " William's hoarse voice called out in the night. The bloodthirsty goddess insinuated herself into his sick brain. While they labored at his bedside, Victoria May, Emma and John came to know it was Kali who symbolized the darkness of India to

William; the tragedy of Cora Stiger; the coming of plague and famine; the death of Mary. In his heated delirium he fancied the goddess trying to kill him, kill progress, kill the fresh and new and good that threatened her regime of blood and ignorance in India.

" He's worked himself almost to death," groaned Victoria May as she grieved over the writhing figure on the bed, while with a pounding heart John fought to save the life of the suffering doctor.

In her safely-distant quarters from the sick-room Zizabai crooned to the restless child in her arms, " Go to sleep, missy-baba, . . . go to sleep . . ." while a vaguely uneasy atmosphere hung over the hospital grounds and anxious, worried villagers milled through the compound day and night, awaiting further word of the Doctor-sahib. In their comfortable new home lepers knelt before the Christians' God and implored His blessing upon the man who had shown them brotherly love.

The mighty palace at Kolhapur trembled with the Maharajah's anxiety for the doctor.

" India *needs* Dr. Wanless," he insisted. Then with a surge of self-reproach, " I have not shown my gratitude sufficiently."

Some days later, hearing that the doctor was on the road to recovery, he went to him and in a burst of enthusiasm said, " Dr. Wanless, in great appreciation of your services to me, I would like to present a gift to you, hoping you will accept it. It is a

small hospital—a good substantial stone building—
with a doctor's residence and assistants' houses in a
spacious compound situated in my city. Until recently it was used for military purposes but it is suit-
able and ready for your use. Funds for enlarging the
building and adding a modern operating theatre are
with the gift. For a long time I have been desirous of
having you start medical work in my State and running it on the same Christian principles that you do in
Miraj. I give this gift in memory of your beloved
wife," the Maharajah said. " My memorial to her."

Thus the Mary Wanless Memorial Hospital came
into existence, showering blessings on suffering
womanhood and reaching fingers of mercy even into
the zenanas and the palaces where timid women
could not venture out and brave the gaze of men.

Not satisfied yet, with this expression of esteem, the
Maharajah thought of other Christian principles to
put in effect. He called his munshi. " Write what I
tell you and see that it is delivered to the newspapers
and displayed in a public place." Straightening his
massive shoulders he added, " This is a Kolhapur
State Public Notice! " and proceeded to dictate.

Three days later the native state of Kolhapur
frothed and erupted as news of the Public Notice
spread from the bazaar into homes, through court-
yards, over the fields. The different castes were
divided in opinion as to their ruler's reasonableness.

" The Maharajah has turned against us! "

" The Maharajah recognizes progress! "

" He turns from the way of his people! "

" He knows what is best for India."

They argued the question pro and con. But the Maharajah sat firmly upon his throne and gazed with pride upon his proclamation.

> " Be informed that, at all public buildings, charity rest houses, state houses, public government inns, etc., and river watering places, public wells, etc., no defilement on account of any human being is to be taken account of. Just as in Christian hospitals and schools, and as *Wanless, Doctor-sahib,* in the American Mission, treats all with the same love, so also here they are to be treated as not esteeming any unclean."

Brahmins stormed their protests. " His Highness is unreasonable! The untouchables are but as filthy dogs. We cannot treat them otherwise! They can never be our equals! "

The untouchables wondered with awe, " Are we really to be allowed to draw water from *any* Brahmin's well? " And they whispered among themselves, fearful of trickery, unable to believe that equality was desired for them. They had never, in all their lives, heard a suggestion of such a thing.

But the Maharajah merely smiled. He had known from the first that it would be impossible to enforce the law. However, it was a step forward. It would make his people think—think of the foolishness and

futility of caste. And meanwhile he was helping
Dr. Wanless by publicly sanctioning his Christian
actions.

When word of William's illness came to the Sangli
Mission, Mrs. Greyson cried. Her husband tried to
comfort her.

" He'll be well again," the stooped man said to his
wife, but she insisted, " He worked too hard. If he'd
only had more help."

Mr. Greyson nodded, awkwardly patted his wife's
plump shoulder, but behind his thick-lensed glasses
an idea was taking shape.

" I know where we can get him some help! " he
exclaimed. " I know just the one."

" Whom are you thinking about? " questioned
Mrs. Greyson curiously.

" Not a doctor or nurse," he replied, " but someone
who can do a lot of good at the hospital and fill what
I think is a real need."

" Land sakes, come to the point," she said impatiently. " You're so long-winded, Ezekiel."

He peered down over his spectacles, snapped out
two words and sat back with an expression of accomplishment.

" Lillian Havens! "

" Well . . . ! " Mrs. Greyson sat up straight,
gasped. " Why didn't I think of her myself? Of
course, she's just the one! " Here a trace of doubt

wiggled into her voice. " Do you think Kolhapur station can spare her? "

" Dora," the grey-haired missionary blew on his glasses, polished them off with his handkerchief, " there isn't a mission station in India that would withhold one thing from William Wanless." With that he adjusted his glasses, put on his hat and went out.

Life stepped up to a sunnier tempo at Miraj hospital. Because of patient, devoted care the doctor was getting well. John, Emma, and Victoria May, weary from their struggle with death and the demanding work of the hospital, found renewed energy in William's returning health.

As the warmth of the season closed about him, a strange new sound came to the doctor's ears. Propped up comfortably in an armchair, he listened closely. The sound was unmistakably organ music— and not the kind played by Victoria May. This was sweet and melodious. He leaned forward, peered out the window of his bungalow living room across the compound toward the children's ward from where the music was coming. The stirring melody of " Jesus, Savior, Pilot Me," flooded across the warm air and reverberated through his quiet room.

He gripped the arm of his chair. " I can't be imagining this." He reminded himself that his fever had broken, the delirium past. But that music!

". . . over life's tempestuous seas . . ."

Humming and tapping out the time with his fingers, the convalescing doctor gradually abandoned himself to the compelling sweetness of the familiar hymn.

" William! "

Victoria May's voice cut through the room. William shook himself. He must have fallen asleep. Was that someone calling, he asked himself.

" Our new evangelist has arrived." There was anticipation in Victoria May's voice. " I want you to meet her." Gesturing toward a figure who had just entered the door, she said, " This is Lillian Havens."

As he turned his head toward the doorway, William had his first glimpse of the young widow from America.

" You were playing that music." William's words were a statement. He didn't ask. He knew.

" Yes," she said smiling. " I hope I didn't bother you."

It was with extreme satisfaction that Victoria May watched the first smile since the day of his illness warm William's face. It twinkled and then shattered into laughter.

" Bother? " He threw back his head and laughed heartily. " My dear lady, it was a tonic! "

Victoria May put her arm about the slender waist of the new assistant. " She's been in the Kolhapur mission station for six months, but when the Greysons heard of your overwork they prevailed upon her to come to Miraj." Victoria May's rigidity formed a distinct contrast to Lillian's fluid grace. "Lillian's very popular with the native people, as you can well imagine." She permitted herself the luxury of a smile. "And—she'll supply us with all our music!"

William chuckled. How glad Victoria May was to be relieved of her enforced thumping at an old wheezy organ each Sunday. "Good!" he boomed. "The native people respond to music. They like it." He hesitated and a playful note crept into his voice. "And to tell the truth—so do I."

The women both laughed.

"I thought I could work with the children," explained Lillian. "Miss Hastings told me the children's ward is always filled, and then there are other children who belong to patients here. Music could bring them very close to the spiritual side of your work—and keep them out of mischief at the same time," she added with an irresistible smile. William was suddenly struck with the blueness of her eyes. "Like two pieces of stray sky," he thought to himself quite unexpectedly.

And then he felt quite pleased with life. He had three new assistants . . . and good ones. Emma, the nurse; John, the doctor; and Lillian, the music-maker. William settled back in his chair. He no longer felt himself to be a foreign body battling for existence on India's soil, but like the banyan tree he had cast and recast roots, sap and bough, deep into the land, while the land in turn nourished and sustained him.

Victoria May, chafing under the slowness of convalescence, awaited impatiently a time to tell William of her idea for future doctors' training at Miraj. The opportunity came the day after Lillian's arrival. As usual her approach was abrupt, without preliminary.

"William," she began, giving him a bowl of hot chicken soup, "I have an idea."

He took the soup eagerly, noting with satisfaction the return of his appetite. "An idea?"

The starched, crisp woman was glad of his good humor. "Yes. Why don't you start a doctors' training school? Right here at the hospital."

He took a spoonful of the soup, enjoying its flavor. "Go on." His voice was encouraging.

"Well, I haven't thought out the details. But there's no doubt about it, one man can't keep up the work of this hospital—not the way it's growing."

"I have John," he reminded her.

"John Holmes is only one man. He can get sick or he can die or he can even get married and leave."

William was amused at her sequence of thought. How surprised she'd be, William mused, if she knew that all during my convalescence I've been considering this very thing. He had visualized not only a medical class but a school where he could train young Indians. He checked his thoughts. He wanted to hear Victoria May's plans.

"Mmmm," murmured William into his soup.

He could almost feel her bristle at his apparent lack of interest, knew she was trying to keep a grip on her sharp tongue and he enjoyed his little game. "I *must* be getting better," William thought to himself, " to want to tease her this way."

Victoria May's tiny nurse's cap quivered on her greyed hair. " There's absolutely no sense in you working yourself to death! " she declared, and burst out, " Suppose you had died, what then? "

William kept an innocent expression on his face. " I might have gone to Heaven," he suggested.

She snorted, then glanced at him quickly. " William Wanless," she drew her face into a most foreboding expression, " are you making light of me? "

At the sight of her assumed fury, William could contain himself no longer and burst into hearty laughter.

" Don't spill that soup," cried Victoria May, snatching the rocking bowl from his hands. " If you ask me," she declared, " you're all well! "

William got up from the cane chair, adjusted his robe and stood on his two feet. " I feel like a new man," he declared heartily and took several tentative steps about the room. " I think I can very soon begin working again."

" Now, don't go wearing yourself out," she scolded. " And before you so much as stir I want you to give your word that you'll do something about more help."

William sat down, conscious that the surge of health he had felt had been but a promise. " All right," he said. " Just to please you I'll give my word."

It was not easy laying plans for this important new step, and William, John, and Victoria May had long conferences during which each phase of the new work was considered. Who would be eligible for doctors' training? Victoria May and John favored the training of interested young men from Canada, England or America, but William's words were prompted by his vision of the future of India.

" Someday," he said, " the Indian people will have home rule. The desire for freedom is already stirring in their hearts, but they must be ready.for it. We're not going to help them by importing foreigners to do their work. We can only help India by teaching her people to help themselves."

" And who is going to pay for their keep while they're studying? " Victoria May's mind always considered the practical side.

William had an answer. " We'll take care of them out of hospital funds. There's no reason why Miraj hospital can't realize enough to pay for training new doctors."

" But do you think you can find native men able to take this training? " she insisted, thinking of the system of caste, the illiteracy and superstition of the country.

But William was thinking of the dissatisfied young people of India who were impatient with the old ways, groping for the new. " They must have a foundation upon which to build these new ways," he said over and over. " If I can train young Indians to give relief, physically and spiritually, to their fellow man, it will be my greatest contribution to this country."

His mind teemed with plans. He could write other missionaries in India and ask them to send educated native Christians for medical training. His school would offer such excellent training that it would one day be affiliated with the Medical College of Bombay. The young doctors could go back to the mission stations prepared to bring medical aid to the great village population of India. The fact that nearly ninety per cent of the educated physicians lived in the cities and large towns troubled William deeply. His students would minister to the sufferers of the villages.

And so it was decided to start a training school for the medical education of Indian youth. William would be their instructor while John carried on the routine work at the hospital. All classes would be given in the morning to permit William to do surgery in the afternoon.

As the plans were made, Victoria May realized with a shock that the doctor's work would be increased instead of decreased, at least until the first graduates emerged which would be something like a period of four years. She shook her head as the indefatigable William swept into action like a western monsoon.

Visions of the future filled his mind: pictures of

his adopted people spreading knowledge and healing from village to village, from the Bombay Presidency north to the Punjab, east to the great river Ganges, south to Ceylon. His mission became increasingly clear. The man from the West must come to share, to give to the East what good he has found in life. The idea of branch dispensaries and hospitals came into the doctor's mind. He would build them in Nerla, Avali, Nipani, Ashta, and Vita, and man them with trained Indian doctors from Miraj. The work of this medical centre would spread and grow and multiply—perhaps someday over *all* India.

But as his nimble mind raced ahead with plans, reality—stolid and defiant—blocked his pathway.

Where were the students? Where were the young men with some small education who desired to serve as Christian doctors? Where were the Indian lads who would be willing to give four years of their lives in preparation for a ministry of healing?

William doggedly persisted in his search for training material, until at last, to the astonishment of all his associates, he gathered about him a class of seven youthful Indians.

" They're not very keen," he told John, " nor have they much education, but you wait. Someday we'll train the cream of India's medical crop here. These boys are just the beginning."

And with all the enthusiasm at his command he started the patience-trying task of enlightening young India.

14

VICTORIA MAY was in mourning. Even before the Bombay papers had arrived carrying the sad news, a special messenger came to the hospital compound, sent by the Rajah of Miraj, with a sorrowful announcement. The beloved Victoria, Queen of the United Kingdom of Great Britain and Ireland, and Empress of India, had died.

" Queen Victoria—dead! " Victoria May repeated the words over and over again while a frightening emptiness gripped her. " I never saw the Queen," she explained to Lillian, " but there was such a feeling of security just knowing she was on the throne."

In large cities great cannon boomed out salutes to the royal dead. Throngs of sorrowing people over all India fasted in honor of the Queen whose love and concern for this large portion of the Empire was felt by English and Indians alike. Flags bowed their heads at half-mast while in Miraj the sad-hearted Victoria May shrouded her upper arm with a strip of black crepe and went about her duties heavy-laden.

" Come now, Victoria May, you can't continue to mourn, you know." It was Lillian, fresh and charming as the morning.

The older woman looked up from her chota hazri while a smile tugged at her lips. " Why shouldn't I mourn when my beloved Queen has died? I suppose you're trying to put me in a good mood for your musical tonight."

Lillian seated herself, nodded her thanks for a cup of tea, then replied, " As a matter of fact, I am."

" Hmmm." Victoria May stirred her tea vigorously. " May I ask *why* the musical? "

" Of course." Lillian's smile was disarming. " It's a surprise for Dr. Wanless."

" What kind of surprise? "

" Well," Lillian dipped sparingly into a handwrought silver sugar bowl, " if you promise not to give it away I'll tell you."

Victoria May nodded her promise.

" I've trained a quartet of four of our medical students and they're going to sing songs."

" Well! "

" Now don't scold me for taking their time to learn to sing," Lillian coaxed. " They have good bass and tenor voices and love to sing."

" I'm not scolding you," Victoria May hastened to explain. " It's just that I think it's such a good idea I have no words to express myself." She bit off a piece of toast, then added with a wry smile, " If the students receive both medical and musical training it won't be long before every aspiring student of medicine in India will want to come to Miraj."

" I don't know about that," smiled Lillian, " but I do think Dr. Wanless is going to be surprised at his versatile students."

Before there was time for a reply a gentle voice,

raised in urgency, was heard above the sound of
rapping on the door.

"Missi-sahib! Missi-sahib!"

Victoria May recognized the voice.

"Come in, Sitabai."

The faithful little woman appeared in the doorway,
breathless from a hurried trip across the compound.

"Doctor-sahib says for you to please come now,"
she gasped.

"What's that?" Victoria May cocked her good
ear.

"Doctor-sahib wants you now, please."

"I'll be right there," the prim spinster replied as
she excused herself and hurried from the bungalow.
When the doctor called it was important. Victoria
May had learned that early in her nursing career.

She dashed across the compound. It must be an
emergency case, she thought as she looked about, expecting to see Emma Harries also hurrying toward
the hospital building. But Emma was nowhere in
sight. If anything's happened to our head nurse, she
groaned and hastily dismissed the thought. But
what can William want this early in the morning?

"Well?"

As she faced the doctor, Victoria May knew she
looked like a frightened chicken with her clothes awry
and an errant lock of hair straggling over one ear.
Expecting to see William furrow-browed over a
serious emergency, it was something of a let-down to
find him seated in his desk chair looking at her with

mischief in his eyes. Behind him stood a native pair, a man and wife, plainly anxious and puzzled.

" Victoria May," he chuckled, " what would you say was the matter with this good woman? "

Her eyebrows jumped in surprise. William Wanless, who could usually diagnose a case with one look, was asking her advice.

" Don't you know? " gasped the spinster, but William only repeated his question.

" What would you say was the matter with her? "

One glance at the uncomfortable woman told the story. " As the natives say," she began, " her foot is heavy."

He nodded. " Exactly."

" But why ask —— " Before she could finish her question, he answered.

" These people have come all the way from Bombay. A doctor up there diagnosed her case as a tumor. They came to Miraj for me to operate."

" A tumor? " Unbelief strained at Victoria May's voice. " But in India where babies are born all the time, everywhere —— "

" It's the same desperate, crying need of medical knowledge! " The doctor's voice shook. " Sending these people all the way down here unnecessarily. And the expense! They'll probably be in debt to some money lender for years to come! "

" It's a shame," she agreed energetically. " But then this woman has more reason to be here than lots of others who've made the trip. They think they're dying," her lips closed tightly, "and you've cured them with a good dose of salts!"

William smiled at her expression. "I've been thinking," he began, "of running up to Bombay once a month. I could take a hotel room for an office, hold clinics for a couple of days and ——" but he was cut off by Victoria May's impatient voice.

"William Wanless, if you're thinking of taking on any further activity . . . just after you've started your student training . . ." Her voice broke with vexation. She shouldn't have brought up this problem at all.

"It's far better for one man to go to Bombay once a month than for a thousand to come down to Miraj."

"But you haven't time."

"I'll make time." He was thinking of the large numbers he could benefit, and at the same time relieve the congestion of his overflowing wards. He could give examinations, advice, and prescriptions, sending only those in need of surgery or hospital care to Miraj. He made his decision. "I'll start the end of this month."

She glared. "You'll have another breakdown," her voice warned ominously, yet she knew his determination and that when William Wanless decided to do a thing, he would always see it through.

William smiled at her clouded face and turned his attention to the patients at hand. "Here, take this woman to a ward, and tell her husband he can stay in the compound. I see he's brought his blanket."

As the elderly nurse fretted off with her new charges William laughed. Occasionally she was like a mother, but more often she was like an old hen clucking over a favored chick, and he was that chick.

" I think I'll shave off my beard," William said to himself. " When she sees that I have a chin it may stop her clucking."

He was still chuckling about the proposed removal of his beard as he started his daily work. First he made the hospital round. A vigor seemed to possess William as he opened the door of the ophthalmic ward. " I'm like a fireman's horse when he hears the bell," he had once confessed to the Maharajah. " The sight of sick people makes me want to be busy. I want to cure every one of them right away! "

His coming was heralded by a native nurse. " Here comes the Doctor-sahib," she whispered and like a quick, buzzing fly the news flew from bed to bed. Bandaged heads trembled expectantly.

" Good morning! Good morning! " William's voice was as hearty as his appetite. " Doctor-sahib." His name was uttered by voices of all description, and they blended like a blessing in his ears. Fluttering hands waved a welcome as they listened for the footsteps of the man they could not as yet see.

" Somebody gets rid of his bandages today," the doctor's voice was jocular. " Who is it? "

Exclamations quivered in the air as the nurse brought charts, operation records.

" Today for me, Doctor-sahib."

" Today, me, too . . . please. Please."

The pleading voices rose around him. " Now, now. No impatience. You've all been blind a long time. It's worth a few days' patience to treat your eyes right so you can see again. Ah, Madame Alexandra Mastakovich! "

" Yes! "

The vibrant word came from a bed at the end of the ward. William filled with a sense of satisfaction as he remembered her case. She had been brought to Miraj by her husband, both Catholics and both of them in the throes of despair.

" We have traveled all the way from Russia," cried the husband remembering the long trip through Persia, the tedious boat ride through the Persian Gulf. " We came for a miracle of healing at Goa. We prayed and prayed at the tomb of our patron Saint, Francis Xavier, but all to no avail. He didn't hear our prayers."

The lovely sightless woman had stopped her husband with a gentle reproach. " Please, Ivan. Perhaps our prayers were not right. Perhaps . . ."

But the husband burst in furiously, and William could see tears of disappointment in his eyes. " For fifteen year we save our rubles for the miracle. We hear of the healings at St. Francis Xavier's tomb at Goa. They tell us, ' every twelve year the tomb is open, you need only to kneel and pray before his remains and your wife will see again.' So we come all the way to Goa, we wait in the crowds for a week to enter the tomb, we kneel before him in his gold casket, we pray, kiss his toes. But still my wife is blind!" His voice broke off in anguish.

"A fellow traveler at Goa told us of you, Doctor Wanless." The wife's voice was kindly to hear after the harshness of her husband's. "This man said, 'You have prayed here for days and your Saint has not performed the miracle of healing. Why don't you go to the living Saint?' 'Who is the living Saint?' I asked. And he replied, 'The Miracle-man of Miraj.'" Her lips trembled. "And so we have come to you, Dr. Wanless. Can you give me my sight? Can you make it possible for me to see again?"

As William had looked into their pleading faces a sense of intense humility overcame him. The woman had cataracts. A local anesthetic, a few moments on the operating table, three days with bandages, and she would have her sight. "Thank God their faith can be rewarded," he had murmured as he assigned the woman to an hour for operation.

And now the day had come for the bandages to be removed. As he approached the Russian woman he noticed that she was trembling. Her hands shook with eagerness and apprehension. And then William saw that her husband came up near the bed. The man's face was white, the muscles in his jaws worked feverishly, yet he said nothing. The doctor leaned over the woman and as he loosened the bandages spoke. "Lift your eyes slowly, carefully. And don't be afraid." The bandage fell and William saw that her forehead was wet with perspiration. Slowly, slowly she lifted her eyelids. At first there was a blur, then gradually the eyes focused. She could make out the form of a man, a man standing at the foot of her bed. His image became clearer . . . clearer.

" Ivan! " she shouted. "I can see! I can see! "

He swooped to her side and they clung together as she searched his face over and over, looking into eyes she had not seen for so many years.

William turned away, his heart straining with gratitude for the healing, restoring ability of his hands. The ward reverberated with excited voices aroused by the triumph in the woman's shout, as William approached another and then another who today would experience the miracle for themselves.

After the eye ward the maternity ward was next, and after that the men's surgical, women's surgical, then the children's, each with its own kind of miracle, only a few with tragedy and sadness. And every single patient knew the Doctor-sahib as a friend.

William looked at his gold watch. Half-past nine. Time for his medical students. As he crossed the compound, first one and then another helper waylaid him. Bhikaji, the compounder, had a question about a prescription; Numretibai, a nurse, came with a chart to tell of the rising temperature of a surgical case; the painter wanted to know which private room he was to whitewash and paint; the carpenter awaited the doctor's orders; a sweeper said the cook had beaten him and he was going to leave; the *pani-walla* said the rope in the well had broken and he couldn't draw any more water; Gopalrao, the engineer, asked to have a new part for the engine sent from Bombay; Gorderao, a clerk, handed him a prepaid telegram and asked what answer to send.

Patiently William answered each one as he proceeded through the compound, passing the daily-assembled crowd of filthy, diseased villagers squatting on the back verandah of the hospital waiting for examination.

" Thank goodness for John," he breathed as he pushed open the door of the anatomical building and prepared to impart knowledge to his youthful students. He thought of them with satisfaction and pride. The carefree Luxmanrao; Nanaji who laughed at the wrong time during lectures; the sturdy brothers Malapparao and Vitoba; Sumitra with the elaborate manners; the nervous Premanik; and Anandrao.

" Good morning! " The doctor's greeting always preceded daily prayer. Beneath his jolly smile this morning lurked a desperate hope that today one of the seven students could name correctly the bones of the human leg. He glanced over the class. The two brothers were missing.

" Anandrao," William fixed his eyes upon the sober face of the Indian youth, " where are the brothers? " This was the one young man upon whom he could depend for factual information; the most

promising student in the class. Two heavy-lidded
eyes gazed upon the doctor and a low voice answered.

" They have gone," he said simply.

" Gone? " A feeling of despondency gripped
William. " Where? "

Anandrao shrugged. " They do not wish to be
doctors. The work is too difficult."

William had a slight skirmish with his temper
before speaking. " Why didn't they speak to me?
They've been living here at our expense, they promised to finish their training. They know how desperately we need doctors at Miraj! "

Nanaji tittered. William bit his lip. It was a mistake to ever show frustration before these people, " to
lose izzat " the Indians called it. His fingernails dug
into his palms, but when he spoke his voice was cool.

" If there are others who contemplate leaving,
please do so now. Otherwise I shall expect you upon
your honor to finish this course which you have
started." He looked into each face, desperately hoping that none would go. It was Luxmanrao, the carefree, whose eyes fell before the searching glance of
the doctor.

" Doctor-sahib," he began and William recognized
the all-Indian tone of apology, " my father is very
unhappy with so much work to do in the fields, and he
thinks I should help him instead of you."

" Your father? " questioned William, recalling
vaguely that this boy was the son of a widow. The
low, furtive glances of amusement between the other

students verified his suspicions. "I thought your father was dead."

But the youth showed no embarrassment. Instead he merely smiled broadly and gurgled, "Yes, Doctor-sahib."

William passed his hand over his face. This was a herculean task, fitting young Indians for hospital work. "I hope there will be some left," he thought as the four years' training loomed ahead like eternity and his dreams for multiplying himself through Indian students appeared hopeless. If they all dropped out . . . if there were none to help him. But William could not permit himself the luxury of worry. He shook his head, squared his shoulders, and lectured until twelve o'clock noon.

"Send my lunch into the office," he instructed Victoria May. "I won't take time to eat at the bungalow."

"Why not?"

He could almost fancy her clucking. He twinkled inside. Wait until this evening when he appeared at the musical function without his beard. He drew his brows together.

"I'm going to look in at the leper home. Tell Emma Harries to have the operating theatre ready for half-past one."

He noted with satisfaction that she said nothing, though she did clench her teeth.

William pedaled the two miles on his bicycle. As

he entered the ground surrounding the leper home he became aware of the careful planting of flowers and shrubs. Bright red hibiscus lifted their open faces to the sun, gorgeous-hued zinnias hugged the pleasant building, while oleander trees, in a profusion of white and pink blossoms, dotted the yard.

Rama, working among the flowers, hailed the doctor's coming. Suddenly the yard was peopled with patients.

A visitor less compassionate than William would have been shocked and revolted, for leprosy eats its victim slowly and crumblingly. In some cases only fingers were gone, but often hands, forearms, feet, legs, and even faces were horribly mutilated by this most loathsome of diseases. And yet—warm and cheerful smiles appeared on the lips of these patients. They gave William a twinge of wonder. Doomed to die a miserable and lingering death, they looked as lighthearted as children playing in the streets. "The redemptive, regenerating power of love," the doctor murmured to himself as he enthusiastically inspected their garden.

Later he spoke with them, examined the progress of the disease of each one, gave instructions for treatment and encouraging words. And now there was but one patient left to examine—Rama.

William had known for some time that the young man was responding to the treatments, but had not raised his hopes for fear of a setback, but today, after a careful, minute examination, the truth became apparent. All symptoms of the disease had disappeared. The doctor looked into the soft brown eyes of the patient, never-complaining Rama, and with his words gave him release.

" You're cured, Rama. You may be discharged from the leper home."

Two brown eyes stared unbelievingly. Had he heard the Doctor-sahib aright? " Cured? " he repeated, as if unable to grasp the meaning of the word.

William smiled. " You no longer have leprosy."

Rama stared at his foot, then at the doctor.

" Doctor-sahib," his voice trembled, " I am like— like I was before? " It was so hard for him to understand that he was well.

" Like you were before," came the calm assurance.

Rama's eyes filled with sudden, unexpected tears, and then he was on the matting, prostrated before William.

" You are my God! You are my God," sobbed Rama over and over, his body throbbing with adoration. The terrible relief, the strange, wild thrill of release from horrible death shook him and he kissed the feet of his deliverer with furious ecstasy.

Tears came to William's eyes, too, as he felt the gratitude of a soul delivered into life. He put firm hands on the quivering shoulders.

" Rama! Rama, up on your feet! "

But the grateful one lay before him, his body shaking.

" Rama! " William permitted sternness to creep

into his voice. Instantly the sensitive Indian lifted his face. Had he displeased his Doctor-sahib? Quickly Rama scrambled to his feet, the pain of anxiety torturing his features. As they stood facing each other, William let the smile come to his face. His arm closed about the shoulder of the one before him.

" It is not I," he quoted gently, " but the Father within me."

Rama nodded, ashamed. He had forgotten the teaching of his Bible. He had called the Doctor-sahib God.

Back in the operating theatre, equipped with two tables since the coming of John Holmes, William had scrubbed his hands, donned his sterilized gown and cap and except for rubber gloves and mask was ready to start the afternoon's operations.

" How many today? "

William's voice in surgery always reminded Emma Harries of the hymn, " Onward Christian Soldiers." " He barks just like a major," she confided to Victoria May, but they both understood that a man with fifteen to twenty operations in an afternoon must be keyed to the highest pitch of his efficiency.

She consulted her list. " Thirty-one operations today."

With a flash of humor William turned to John who was donning his rubber gloves. " I was right. Odd number today. Even yesterday." John grinned.

The door opened and Anandrao came in, dressed in a long white surgical apron. He was the first student to be used in the operating room and William noted with a glow of pleasure the youth's alertness. Nodding curtly to the young man, William gave instructions.

"This table contains the sterilized instruments. When I am through with an instrument you will place it over on the table by the wall—not back with the sterilized ones. Do you understand?"

Anandrao nodded. "Yes, Doctor-sahib." His voice was so low it was merely a whisper.

Someday, thought William, there will be more operating rooms, and they will be attended by Indian doctors. His thoughts were broken into by John who approached him with troubled eyes.

"Dr. Wanless," he began, then faltered.

"Yes?" William glanced curiously at John's troubled face.

"There's a tumor case today," the young man continued. "I—I think you'd better take it."

William stared. "Why?"

"Well," John flushed, "I haven't done a tumor yet."

"You've worked with me, haven't you?"

John bit his lip. "Yes, but that's different."

William leveled a firm, steady glance upon the hesitant young doctor. "You'll take the tumor patient," and with these words dismissed him from his side.

Mildred Mumford hurried into the room, ready to

assist at minor tasks. Miss Mumford was gradually abandoning herself to spinsterhood. Since receiving news that her Alfred had married another woman, she decided that men were fickle and that she would devote her life to good works. " It's too bad but she'll never make a decent surgical nurse," William had prophesied as he and Emma Harries once tried to teach her surgical routine. " She's too slow and can't even anticipate a sutured needle." But nurses were not plentiful so Miss Mumford filled in at various tasks and believed that she, personally, was saving half the lives in India.

William glanced about the spotless, white-tiled room. Anandrao stood grimly by, John chewed nervously on his lip contemplating the tumor operation, Miss Mumford twisted about on one foot, while dependable Emma Harries stood waiting for his words. He nodded his head. " Ready," he said and heard John's sharp intake of breath as the first two patients were wheeled in.

John's first was a simple tonsilectomy, while William's was a serious abdominal operation. Permitting his bullock to sleep in his hut, a farmer had been gored by the animal during the night, and had been brought to the hospital, his protruding bowels wrapped in filthy rags. The operation was difficult, dangerous, and demanded the utmost skill. As he finished with his first instrument, William quickly passed it toward his sober-faced medical student. There was a pause. Anandrao was staring at the

wound, fascinated and horrified. With an exclamation of impatience William thrust the instrument
upon the youth. The boy flushed, turned and laid it
with the sterilized instruments. William was bending over his patient . . . his fingers skilful and sure,
when he saw the action that made his taut nerves
snap. With a roar he snatched up the bloody instrument from the sterilized table and slammed it down
on the marble floor.

" I told you not to put used instruments with the
sterilized ones! " he shouted at Anandrao, then went
on with his work.

Anandrao, scared and shaking, seemed incapable
even of thought. How could he have made such a
stupid mistake? Why hadn't he followed directions?
But as suddenly as it had come, the anger went out
of the doctor's eyes and they became impersonal,
busy, occupied only with the work at hand.

John had finished his fourth operation when the
tumor sufferer was wheeled in by ward-boys.

William bent busily over his patient. " Gauze."
His voice moved Emma Harries to instant response,
but she noticed with tightly-drawn lips that his eyes
twinkled and he occasionally glanced toward the form
of nervous Dr. John.

John looked at his patient with the great, bulging
tumor, then turned impulsively toward William. The
older doctor was apparently too engrossed in the
task before him to be aware of a crisis in the younger
man's life.

"More ether." John's voice sounded tremulous in the quiet of the white, tense room as he gave his directions to Miss Mumford. Once more he turned imploringly, but there was no response so John gulped, turned to his patient.

With a quick, sideways glance William noted with keen satisfaction that the younger doctor took a deep breath, squared his jaw, and commenced to operate.

Later in the evening another kind of operation was taking place and in William's bungalow. He was removing his beard. John had sauntered in, and finding William shaving walked about the warm room, his hands pulling at his coat lapels.

"Proud of your tumor operation today?" William asked putting down a pair of scissors then lathering his face.

John sighed. "I don't know how I ever got through it, much less the patient. But," his voice held an unaccustomed ring of assurance, "we both survived."

There was a pause broken only by the scraping of a straight-edge razor over the older doctor's cheek. Wiping the lather on a piece of paper he queried, "Would you feel finicky about tackling another one?"

"No, I wouldn't," replied the young man. "In fact," a new poise seemed to settle over him, giving him a becoming touch of maturity, "after that operation I'm not afraid to tackle anything."

" Just as I thought," murmured William cleaning his face of all adornment except a neatly-trimmed moustache. He stepped back from the mirror. " Well, how do I look? "

John stared. " Say! what do you know about that? You look ten years younger! "

The beardless one cocked his head, stroked his bare chin. " It feels a lot cooler, I can tell you that."

John sighed with elaborate melancholy. " I know that I won't have a chance with the girls now—especially if they see you first." William roared with laughter.

" By the way," asked the younger doctor curiously, " what happened to Anandrao today? " He recalled the violent scene in the operating theatre.

William smiled. " Got excited. Lost his head. But," he patted his valiant moustache, " I talked with him afterward. Told him I wasn't angry, just impatient. And I told him, as I've told you, that I believe my strict antiseptic precautions account for much of my surgical success and I won't brook any carelessness in that regard. But—he's all right now." And then to bolster up his fast-ebbing faith in his native students added, " Anandrao's a good boy. He'll make a fine doctor . . . someday." His voice trailed off wistfully as he looked at his watch. He had half an hour or more in which to go over his accounts. Taking a final look in the mirror at his almost forgotten face, he settled down to work. John sat down in an easy chair to wait for the doctor.

" The musical's supposed to start at eight-thirty,"
complained John impatiently to the doctor bending
over his desk.

William blinked, leaned back in his chair. " Time
goes too fast," he said and closed his ledger. " I'll
have to take care of the rest of my accounts later in
the evening."

" You really need a bookkeeper," worried the
young Nova Scotian, thinking of the long, tedious
night hours William spent keeping his accounts
straight.

William sighed. " Yes, I need a bookkeeper, a
half-dozen more doctors, twenty or so nurses, and a
secretary for my correspondence. But ——" His
voice accepted the inevitable responsibility of overworked missionaries as he got up from his desk and
donned his dinner coat.

" Why don't you let me keep your books ? " John's
offer was genuine, but the doctor only smiled.

" You stick to your medicine, young man," he
advised. " If you learn half there is to know about
Indian ailments you won't have time to bother with
anything else. Well," he drew a deep breath, put
aside duties and prepared to enjoy a rare evening of
relaxation, " we'd better get along to that musical."

The living room of the bungalow which housed
Victoria May and Lillian glowed graciously as the
two men approached. Lighted windows revealed
welcomed guests in an atmosphere of friendliness
and well-being. Tender music from a new piano

drifted out to meet them and William twinged with a feeling of nostalgia.

There was the warmth of home here. There was a woman who could brighten up even the darkness of a tropical night with her smile and charm. William felt a deep surge of loneliness.

It was not until he had stepped into the room that he remembered his missing beard.

"William!" Victoria May was the first to give vent to her amazement. She stood stock still and gasped over and over. "Your face! Your face!"

The medical students stared, natural restraint tugging at their astonishment, trying to accept courteously and without surprise the Doctor-sahib divorced from his familiar beard.

Mildred Mumford giggled, Emma Harries uttered a gurgling sound, while Lillian, her face alight with pleased surprise, made a remark which stayed in the doctor's mind.

"Dr. Wanless," she exclaimed, "congratulations!"

He wondered exactly what she meant. But one thing was certain. Lillian approved and he found himself glad that she did.

It was after tea and cakes, after the sociable, pleasant chatter, that Lillian announced her surprise.

"This is something you didn't expect, Dr. Wanless," she began hesitantly. "But I hope you'll be pleased." She sat at the piano.

William tried to keep the curiosity from his face. As the light from the table lamp caressed her soft, warm shoulders and her brown hair he found himself thinking, "Whatever she does will please me." Abruptly he turned his attention to the four medical students, who, bowing and grinning, grouped themselves about the piano. Lillian's fingers touched the keys.

> "On a hill far away,
> Stood an old rugged cross . . ."

The doctor leaned forward. It was unbelievable. The voices of his four students blended in rich, pleasing harmony over the sound of the piano.

> "The end of all suffering and pain . . ."

He smiled. They were as well trained as any professional quartet! And how pleasant to hear the rich voices raised in familiar hymns rather than the endless *bhajans* sung to the noisy accompaniment of Indian drums, wooden castanets and brass discs.

William closed his eyes; found himself immersed in a soul-satisfying peace.

Victoria May glanced at the beardless doctor, and a smile of satisfaction lit up her wrinkled face. "William may be smart about most things," she said to herself. "But I'll bet two cookies he doesn't know he's falling in love." And with a smug cluck she squared her shoulders. At last she had something on the doctor.

15

THE SKY overhead was as blue as Lillian's eyes the day William started for Kolhapur. " My first vacation in four years! " he called jubilantly as he climbed into the newest vehicle in Western India—an automobile.

Lillian shook a warning finger at the doctor. She could never get used to the sight of the new horseless carriage. She recalled the day, three weeks before, when William had jiggled into the hospital compound with his wonderful new gift sent from America. " Why, it looks just like a top-buggy," she had exclaimed. " Except that it needs a horse."

Natives, scared out of their wits at the appearance of the strange contraption, had shunted about the rapidly-filling courtyard shrieking to newcomers of the magical cart which moved without being drawn by a horse, bullock, or even a man. Speculation had run high. What was it? It must have magic. Some were frightened, others resentful. India did not want such things. A tonga was good enough. Two men threw mud at the auto's shiny side and were immediately jumped on by lusty youths who admired the new vehicle.

They had swarmed about the new car which stood tall and proud bearing the name of H. K. Holsman

Co., New York State. Its wheels were high with slender wooden spokes and solid rubber tires. Its night eyes were small portable kerosene lanterns suspended on hooks on either side of the dashboard. William had investigated and discovered that the car was run by a battery. Anticipating the time when the battery would be no more, he decided it would be possible to put in dry cells of caustic.

"How does it go, Doctor-sahib?" Anandrao had gasped, spellbound before its splendor.

A thorough examination of the car had made William familiar with its operation, but as he turned to explain it to his medical student, the doctor hesitated. With a sigh he remembered the previous four years in which he had dinned and shouted and repeated and repeated medical terms to the youths whose memories seemed to be like sieves. And then he had considered the futility of describing the intricacies of the new automobile. "I'm afraid that would take another four years," he had said to Anandrao, "but if you like you may take a ride with me." "Thank you, Doctor-sahib, but I have work to do!" And with a frightened smile the youth had departed into the hospital. William had finally induced Lillian and Victoria May to go for a ride and the air had been pierced with the older woman's shrill cries. "Don't go so fast! You'll run away with us!" And William had laughed exultantly as the car sped along at fifteen miles an hour, its solid rubber tires bumping along the road, giving a feeling of luxury

compared with the bone-shattering vibrations of a
tonga.

And now William was starting out in the automobile for Kolhapur to join the Maharajah for his
first tiger hunt. He had experienced a grateful thrill
of release when John, Lillian, Emma Harries and
Victoria May had convinced him that they could
carry on at Miraj for a short time while he took a
vacation.

" Have a good time," called Lillian and his other
helpers as he turned out of the compound, onto the
dirt road to Kolhapur.

" I will." He waved back then swerved sharply
to avoid hitting some fleeing natives who shrieked
their terror at the sight of the unbelievable vehicle.

As he drove toward Kolhapur, away from the sickness and antiseptic odors of the hospital, William's
heart seemed to swell. He settled back in the seat,
drew a long breath of sweet country air and looked
for the first time in months at the countryside. After
the rainy season shoots of wheat and millet prickled
the surface of flat, tilled land and formed a bright
green stubble on the red earth. As he left Miraj the
countryside gradually changed. There was more
green. He looked at the pimpurna trees, planted by
the British along the road to afford shade for travelers. Suddenly William came upon the reason for
the everlasting sparseness of these trees. A youthful
shepherd boy, followed by his faithful flock, was
poking at one of the trees with a long, bamboo pole.

A quick, silvery flash at its tip indicated a knife. With a heave the boy severed a slender limb. Bleating their gratitude the sheep received his green offering.

The upper part of the trees, safe from the short boys, trembled thinly, past-victims of casual camels nibbling of their refreshing, available greenness.

As he bobbed past a few bare cottages the doctor heartily wished that the Indian people would adopt the habit of planting trees and flowers. " It would add so much cheer to the landscape," he thought. " But then, all reforms cannot come in a day."

During his leisurely drive the doctor had been aware of an animal browsing ahead at the side of the road. Taking very little notice he started to jog past the beast, when, with a frightened roar, it charged the car.

The impact was terrific. William felt as if the slender vehicle would be overturned. However, it was not the car that was damaged, but the bellowing bull which had broken off a horn when he tangled with his strange opponent.

The snorts of the infuriated beast brought a tattered little man scurrying across a field as he filled the air with indignant shrieks.

" I am ruined! My beautiful animal is desecrated! I am only a poor farmer . . . this bull is all I own! I am ruined! " He beat his skinny chest with horny fists.

William tried to explain the incident, but the bel-

lowing of the frightened bull and the owner's screeching voice gave him no opportunity. It was obvious
that there was but one satisfactory answer to the
situation. Reaching into his pocket, the doctor
brought out some coins. As if by magic the glint of
them dried up the torrent of words. Sunshine broke
out over the Indian's face and as the doctor laid the
money in the grimy brown hand he was repaid with
a deep salaam, honeyed words, and with no further
trouble continued upon his journey.

Two brilliant, screaming parakeets caught his attention and he smiled. The month of March in India
meant the beginning of the marriage season and in
the village of Miraj two and sometimes three marriage ceremonies a day were taking place.

" Let's see," William started counting. " I'm not
so old. Twenty-four when I came. And now I'm
forty-two." And then he smiled. " But somehow,
today, I don't feel that old." He speeded up the car,
thrilling to a dash of excitement, adventure in his
blood.

" By George "—he whacked the steering wheel—
" I think I'll shoot a tiger and bring the skin back to
Lillian! " And his spirits soared eagle-high at the
thought of the intrepid hunter laying his offering at
the feet of his chosen one.

From beginning to end the whole hunting trip
seemed to William like something out of the Arabian
Nights. From the moment of overwhelming welcome

Maharajah's hunt in the jungle.

at the palace in Kolhapur he felt as if he were in a fabulous dream. The Maharajah lavished every attention upon his beloved friend, the miracle-working doctor from Miraj.

" Chee! . . . Chee! " Elephant boys shrilled and excited servants and members of the hunting party twitted like the birds in the forest, as William and the Great King heaved about in the silver howdah atop a great elephant. Heading toward the jungle country, they were passing through a forest tangled with wild lantana. William could see the pink and lavender blossoms peek through twining vines which hung from huge trees like lazy snakes. Feathery tree-ferns unfurled their tender greenness, which mingled daintily with the flowering jasmine. As the doctor relaxed into this primitive beauty he felt as though he were being transported back, back into history while the elephant's dull, heavy feet thudded through the thickening forest and toward the tangled, almost impassable jungle where frailest humming birds mingled with wild boar, and paper-light butterflies caressed the jackal-rent air. The dead silence caused William's flesh to prickle with excitement.

" We'll hunt for the tiger in the night," advised the Maharajah to whom hunting was second nature. " Tonight we shall put out the buffalo calf for bait— and tomorrow night you shall bag your prize. Meanwhile, we can do a bit of hunting this afternoon."

In leaving the palace at Kolhapur William had felt himself to be in the midst of a crowd, for counting the

coolies and elephant boys the group had numbered
fifty. Now, however, in the vastness of the jungle
country, the doctor sensed the smallness of their
number—the frailty of man compared with the
strength and majesty of nature.

" I hope the beaters bring up a kill this afternoon,"
he said. The same thought came to William as
he and the Maharajah sat upon a hastily-erected
machan made of branches and bamboo poles in the
fork of a wide-spreading tree. Rays of sunshine
trailed golden fingers on the dense underbrush and
the doctor discovered himself speaking his heart to
the Maharajah.

" I want a tiger skin to take back to Lillian," he
explained with a smile. " I think she'll appreciate
it." And then to cover his embarrassment, " They're
rather valuable, you know."

But the Maharajah's huge bulk shook and his voice
was filled with laughter. " If I were in your place,
my friend, I should not permit so much time to be
wasted. You have been alone too long," he added
profoundly.

Suddenly the voices of the beaters were raised,
their tom-toms and clashing cymbals shattered a
warning.

" Here they come," cried the Maharajah, then for
William's benefit explained. " The boys have formed
in a semicircle about a half-mile from our clearing
here. As they start closing in they'll drive the

animals toward us." He raised his rifle to his shoulder. "Prepare to shoot."

The drumming, screaming beaters drew nearer . . . nearer. Shrill bird-cries filled the air while chattering monkeys swarmed the branches of trees, coming and going like fantastic figures in a dream. A fox shot through the clearing. A buzzard skimmed heavily over dense foliage. Silently the hunters sat, listening intently.

William's gun rested against his shoulder, the feel of it bringing back memories of boyhood hunts in the Canadian woods. He could hear the thin, nervous wheezing of the Maharajah waiting tensely, expectantly. Leaf-shaped shadows trembled on the gun barrels as an occasional sunbeam drew sharp reflections from their polished surfaces. And now—a stirring in the underbrush. A trembling of the thicket. William felt his heart thudding against his ribs as he waited to see what animal would show itself in the clearing. Another second passed. Then the bushes parted and into the open emerged a full-grown, shaggy black bear.

Before the hulking animal had hesitated a split second the Maharajah's gun roared. The bear dropped to the mulchy ground—dead.

William turned to the Maharajah, a nervous thread of air issuing from between his teeth.

"Wheeew! You gave me a start, Your Highness."

The large man patted the doctor's shoulder apologetically. "I should have waited for my guest," he said, " but I couldn't resist the opportunity of a good shot."

" I'm glad you got him," answered William. " I don't know if I'd been able to bag him or not."

" I promise," the Maharajah vowed solemnly, " to leave the shooting of the tiger to you." Then he unfolded his huge bulk and sighed. " Perhaps we had better leave our hunting now until tomorrow night."

William nodded, smiling, and wondered how the large man had managed to stay curled up on the small *machan* for even a short length of time.

" The boys will tie out the calf tonight," the experienced hunter explained. " And tomorrow morning we'll know if there's a tiger in this area."

William slept lightly that night. He was listening for any sounds that might indicate the presence of a tiger in the vicinity. But nothing came to his ears. " Our camp's too far from the clearing where we tied the calf to hear anything," he told himself, but still couldn't sleep.

At daybreak two excited boys brought back the news.

" The tiger was here last night! "

" He killed the calf! "

" The tiger has come! "

The camp buzzed with excitement. The tiger had killed the calf last night and would return tonight to eat it. William felt himself caught up in exhilaration.

The stage was being set for him—for his first jungle kill.

The day passed quickly. The Maharajah shot a wild boar and a cheeta but William was waiting for night to fall. As the day grew tired the two hunters made their way into the jungle and once more climbed into the tree, seating themselves on the *machan*. As darkness flooded the thick jungle and the moon sought vainly to penetrate its gloom, William and the Maharajah took up their throbbing vigil. Tonight they would bag the tiger. Clammy heat glued William's clothes to his body as they perched high up in the tree, the bloody remains of the buffalo calf below them, alluring bait for the tiger. As the night wore on a vague restlessness seized the thousands of jungle inhabitants causing muffled, unexpected sounds. Like a multi-voiced giant, the jungle tossed and muttered in its sleep.

William quivered with anticipation. Here, under the shrouding branches of this exotic tree, spangled with the light of a tropical moon, and in the company of an Indian Potentate, he experienced a flooding sense of adventure. Excitement prickled at his neck and his breathing trembled heavily. This was an India he had not known before; an India of un-breathed mystery and curious charm. Suddenly he thought of Mary. Now, after all these years, he knew how she had quickened to the allure of the country— to the beckoning of the Taj Mahal. A quick surge of saddening remorse threatened to engulf him but at that moment came a sound!

It was only the snapping of a twig, but it hit William with the impact of roaring thunder. The murky night seemed to quiver, and then with a terrified shriek a small animal scrambled through the underbrush, there was the whoosh of frantic bird wings. The tiger was in the vicinity—the tiger marked for the gun of William Wanless.

William, trained for coolness in a crisis which meant the saving of life, now found himself shaken with a new emotion. He had deliberately pitted himself against a ferocious beast, and meant to take its life. A primitive ecstasy gripped him. " I shouldn't be up in this tree. I should be down on the ground, waiting to come to grips with my enemy." But he remained motionless while his racing heart tore at his chest and a hot passionate surge filled his throat.

Suddenly the Maharajah gasped. William looked down. Out of the darkness flamed two balls of fire. The tiger's eyes. A low, ominous growl sounded, seemed to come out of nowhere, while the balls of fire glowed brightly. And then, as if this moment had been set aside in all eternity, William knew it was time to shoot. A long-dragging second swept his nerves cool and with one movement of his finger the great gun belched forth its fury.

Shrieking, the lank beast clawed thin air. Blood dripped from his side, splashed the earth, smattered a crazy pattern of agonized fury. With a roar that

rent the jungle the tiger lurched in the direction of
the gunshot and without hesitation William again
aimed at the red eyes.

The gun blasted fire. The tiger was still.

There was a breathless pause, then the Maharajah's
voice rang out with pride. "Well, my friend, you
have killed your tiger."

The darkness hid William's pride as he thought of
Lillian accepting the fruits of his hunt.

At dawn, like the swarming of bees, natives
crowded the clearing, laughing, shrieking, trilling
their delight as they eagerly helped themselves to
their promised rewards: the magical whiskers and
charm-evoking claws of the tiger.

William examined the beast. It was mammoth,
beautifully striped, and in the prime of condition.

As the doctor chugged along the road from Kolhapur to Miraj in his car and watched the sane, white
buildings of the hospital loom earnestly out of the distance, he felt a trifle silly. The flamboyant tiger
skin lay docilely in the seat beside him, forming a
strange contrast with the practical little automobile.

William gazed down at his plump, rounding figure.
"Oh, my," he sighed. "I don't know that I'm the
type to accompany a tiger skin." And staring a bit
glumly over the surrounding countryside, he suffered
an obstinate, wistful stab at his heart.

As he turned the car-wheels into the familiar compound, William experienced the calm and complacent

settling down of the " doctor feeling." A million nights away seemed the jungle adventure, while the faint odor of anesthesia gathered him in and seemed to say, " This is your reality. This is your life."

He looked at the tiger skin again and shook his head. " Lillian will probably think I'm crazy."

But Lillian didn't think him crazy. When he laid the skin before her, her heart grew warm and happy and she was in exactly the right mood to say " yes " in answer to the question of the invincible hunter.

16

DECEMBER FIFTH started out as complacently and orderly as any other day for most of the workers at Miraj hospital. John, deep in the work of diagnosis, felt pulses, tapped chests, and examined tongues with the help of three well-trained native doctors. Victoria May ordered Hindu nurses through their morning ward routines. Zizabai prepared to take her young charge, Ethel, for a bargaining session in the village bazaar. To all but William and Lillian, December fifth was just another day in the life of the hospital.

William, in anticipation, had prepared himself when last in Bombay with the purchase of a new formal suit. Buttoning the cutaway coat about his stoutish figure, he stood before the mirror. "Well, this *is* a contrast to my old white everyday suits. Makes me feel like a new man," he chuckled then threw back his rounded shoulders and picked up a comb.

"She's not getting much of a prize," he stated to his semi-bald reflection, and quickly done with the comb patted nervous fingers over his short moustache. Pulling down his coat he stepped back, and looking into the glass surveyed himself objectively for the first time in years.

"Humph. I'm getting a paunch," he observed, then turned and squinted. "All around."

When he had first started putting on weight, Victoria May had remarked: "In India white people get one of two ways. Fat or thin." There had been an envious sigh. "Be thankful, William, that you have a little flesh on your bones."

William shook his head at the image in the mirror. "I guess I'm the type with flesh on my bones, all right," then impatiently dismissed the whole train of thought as being juvenile and irrelevant. He was going to be married and that was that! He sat down in a chair, tapped his fingers on his knee. Then the memory of Lillian's soft, white hands and shoulders crept into his mind and a rosiness seemed to envelop the morning.

"I wish," he announced heartily, "that the carriage would hurry up!"

Lillian studied her flushed cheeks in the mirror and sighed. People would think she was using rouge. "Now, Lillian," she warned herself, "don't, for goodness sake, act like a sixteen-year-old." But her heart refused the advice and continued to pound furiously.

Going to a small writing desk by a window, she opened the top drawer. There were letters, books, mementos and a picture. It was face down. On the stained back was written in brown ink, "Frank Havens, aged twenty-three." She turned it over. A boyish face smiled into her eyes. That ready smile . . . strange how it suddenly bridged the years and she was back again in Dupage, Illinois, in the white-towered church while the organ played " I Love You Truly." Frank was smiling at the altar as she came down the aisle on her father's arm, trembling as her long, tulle veil threatened to catch on the pews.

She seldom permitted herself to think of the tragic sequel to the wedding. A four-weeks honeymoon, then sudden illness, pneumonia had developed, and with cruel, unexpected swiftness the young husband had been taken from her.

She thought of the deep sorrow and how it had led her to the sad little child-widows of India.

Studying Frank's picture a new realization swept over Lillian. So many years had intervened that it now seemed impossible that the youth in the picture had ever been her husband. Somehow . . . today was her only wedding day. She smiled, laid the picture back in the desk, then with infinite care put on her white, lacy wedding hat.

A rap sounded on William's door. " That must be the carriage! " The eager bridegroom jumped up, opened the door.

" Well! "

The figure in the doorway was Anandrao . . . a sad-faced, drooping Anandrao.

" Why are you back here? " demanded William; a

tremor of despair slithered over him like a small crite
snake. He motioned the youth in, closed the door.
Just three weeks before, this same Anandrao, with
head high and eyes flashing, had left for Vita, the only
graduate student entrusted with starting a branch
dispensary.

" Are you sick? " William wanted to shake the
sagging shoulders, to force an answer from the mask-
like face. But Anandrao only sulked and studied the
matting under his feet.

The doctor spoke impatiently. " Anandrao, I'm
leaving in a few minutes." His voice grew stern as
the heavy-lidded eyes continued to dwell upon the
matting. " I'd appreciate it if you'd tell me what's
on your mind . . . and as quickly as possible." He
glanced at his watch. The carriage would be here any
minute.

The thick lids slowly folded back, revealing misery-
laden brown eyes. The usually stolid, emotionless
face quivered.

" I could not do it! I could not do it, Doctor-
sahib! " he cried and buried his face in his tapering
brown hands.

" You couldn't do what? "

" Oh, Sahib," agonized wet eyes appeared from
between taut fingers, " if you could only understand
how hard it is! Here at Miraj we are all Christians
together. We believe the same way. We have no
trouble. But in Vita . . . I am the only Christian.
The people jeer and laugh at me. They call me a

fool!" His voice flooded with tears. "Always before everyone respected me. Now—I am an out-caste!" Bitterness welled up and his tears became scalding hot.

William groaned. His most promising student . . . the young man he had chosen to go out and break the ground among his own people . . . crying and saying it was too hard. "You didn't expect it to be easy, did you, Anandrao?"

The youth shook his head. "I did not know what to expect."

"But we talked it all out. You knew there were no other Christians there. But you also knew you had your medical training. You could help people."

"Yes, Doctor-sahib." But the voice was defeated.

William found his temper mounting. "Now you look here. If your country is ever going to rise out of her ignorance and superstition, it will be men like you who have to help her. India needs brave, fear-less men!"

But the young man only beat his fists upon his heaving chest and cried out, "It is such a sacrifice, Doctor-sahib! Such a sacrifice!"

That word was the spark which set off William's temper. The four years of tedious training, the des-perate need of India, the cowardice and flinching of one who held such promise were stored-up gunpowder to the doctor who suddenly exploded into violent words.

"Sacrifice? *I'm* the one to talk about sacrifice!

Afraid to go ten miles from home . . . right in your own country! " The young man flinched but William roared on. " Didn't I leave my home and come far across the ocean? Your country was strange to me. Yes, and hostile, too! " Kali's bloody hands gripped the doctor's imagination. Years of opposition, struggle, the daily grind of hard work crowded his mind, forced speech from his mouth. " I didn't know your language, your customs or your background. And I was a different color. My wife died here because of the stupidity and carelessness of your people. And I—I——" The doctor ran a suddenly weary hand over his moist forehead, then collapsed into a chair. " Never mind, Anandrao," he murmured hoarsely. " Go away."

The young man, trembling like the leaf on a pipal tree, slipped out the door. William dropped his face in his hands, while his heavy breathing rasped through the room.

" Doctor-sahib . . . Doctor-sahib! " The hurried knock should mean the carriage had arrived. William glanced out the window—then gasped.

Two Arabian steeds, plumed and jeweled, pranced before a coach. And what a coach! Sparkling white, fluted with gilt Oriental carving, it was the Maharajah's own landau used only for special state occasions. Like gleaming pearls on a heap of jewels, the two drivers in scarlet livery and white silk turbans with gold-thread borders sat aloft on a high seat in front. At the back, standing and clinging to the rumble, were two other servants dressed in khaki.

William gave an involuntary chuckle. The Maharajah had asked to provide the bridal conveyance and there it was, shouting aloud His Highness' love of lavish giving.

The doctor shook his head doubtfully. "I'm afraid I'm not nearly romantic enough to go with that," he considered. Another thought crowded his mind, causing elation. "Perhaps I am!" With that he squared his shoulders and went to fetch his bride-to-be.

As the doctor and Lillian hurried toward the carriage, hoping to escape unseen, Victoria May glanced out the window of the maternity ward and gave a scream that became a signal for bedlam. "What is it? What's the matter?" Native nurses ran to her side. John, passing the door, rushed in. Within a minute, before William and Lillian could escape, the compound was alive with frantically-excited well-wishers, who needed no explanation as to what was going on. But before their brisk feet could reach the bridal pair, with a shout and flourish the unbelievable carriage was on its sparkling way.

The very next day, with a like shout and flourish, the story-book coach brought back the doctor and his bride and deposited them at the gate of Miraj hospital.

"Where did you go? Why didn't you tell us? When are you taking your wedding trip?"

Victoria May's questions tumbled so fast she ran out of breath.

Lillian only smiled.

"Well," the doctor began expansively, "we were married at Kodoli by Dr. Graham."

"But where were your wedding bans? I didn't see them posted anywhere. And they have to be posted three weeks before the wedding. That's the law!"

William laughed. "I wrote Dr. Graham a month ago and he posted our bans in his office." His eyes twinkled.

"Where no one but natives would see them," added Victoria May, then grimaced. "William Wanless, you think of everything. But you couldn't keep it a secret from us, could you?" she clucked. "Not with that ice-cream-and-frosting carriage of the Maharajah's."

They all laughed.

"But what about a wedding trip?"

Lillian explained. "William had to come back here. He said that he couldn't leave those critical abdominal cases for very long. After all—we can take a wedding trip later." As William started toward the office Lillian hastily whispered to Victoria May. "When I married this man I married his hospital, too." Her eyes sparkled. "But between you and me I don't mind in the least."

"I'm glad you're back!" John's friendly voice greeted William as he stepped into the office.

" Every time you leave the compound a hundred problems pop up and nobody can solve them but you."

William eased himself into a chair. " What now? " he asked and felt the routine of his demanding work closing in upon him.

" The most important news is about Anandrao."

William sat up straight. " What about him? Where is he? "

John smiled. " I don't know what you said to him yesterday, but as soon as you'd driven off he came to me and asked if he could return to Vita."

" Did he say why? "

" Yes, although I'm not quite sure what he meant. I questioned him thoroughly but all he'd say was, ' I'm willing to make the sacrifice, too. I'm willing to make the sacrifice! ' "

William made no immediate reply. He stood up, walked to a window and gazed into the compound which teemed with activity. His assistant watched, puzzled, as the doctor slowly looked at his two hands, turned them over palms down, flexed them, seemed to glory in their power. Finally he spoke and when he did his voice was husky. " John, what we're doing is mighty hard work, but believe me, it pays the kind of dividends that satisfy! "

❧ 17 ❧

LIKE THE whispered sighs of dancing girls in ancient temples, like a wispy fluff of smoke from a native hookah, like a drop of blood from a sacrifice to Kali, the years roll by in India. Even centuries are fleet, for here antiquity rules with a hand which is immortal.

And yet—from a corner of Southwest India, in the tiny span of forty years—a new way of life was taking hold; a way of life that crumbled caste and healed the sick and taught of Love. And burdened, suffering Indians held out their hands and gathered the new way to themselves as thirsty men reach out for rain.

Forty years before, Miraj had been just another native village—identical with India's thousands of other native villages. But today Miraj was a shrine, a Mecca of healing. And its High Priest was the Doctor-sahib, whose name was magic over all the land. For forty years he had given comfort, healing, words of Christian love. He had sent out hundreds of trained native doctors to multiply and increase this balm which he had brought from across the sea. He never once spared himself from the command of his Master, "Preach the Gospel, heal the sick."

But now—it was time to say good-bye. William had pressed his tight lips tighter when John, a month before, had said, "Your heart." But William knew before that time; knew that it was no longer safe to wield a scalpel or to touch an eye made sightless by a cataract. His heart. "Thank God, I wore out. I didn't rust out!" he boomed, and found great satisfaction in the thought.

And so, for the past month, Southwest India had been busy with an uninterrupted series of events to bid farewell to their own, their beloved, their miracle-working Doctor-sahib.

In Ashta, Kodoli, Bombay, Kolhapur, Nipani, Kurli, Sangli, Miraj, and Poona; in schools, mission stations, tents and auditoriums, whole towns flocked to pay homage to the man who had given his life to them so they might have life more abundant.

William had experienced Indian gratitude at the hospital, but this was different. It seemed to be as boundless and endless as India's population. It gathered momentum, rolled bigger and bigger until he was overwhelmed, overcome with its tumultuous force.

John fussed and fumed as he saw the man he had ordered home, going day and night, traveling by train, motor and tonga to attend the farewell functions of branch hospitals and churches, visit friends and patients, and to be guest of honor at nightly festive occasions. "I'm glad for your health's sake that you're leaving in a few days," he confided to William, who was dressing in his best suit, preparing for the greatest farewell of all—the affair at Poona.

"Don't worry so, John. I'll be all right. And I'm having the time of my life, believe me."

A few days before an invitation had come to the doctor inviting him to be guest of honor at a mammoth public reception planned by the citizens of Poona in his honor. Newspapers and printed placards announced the great farewell reception. Indian notables were to speak, the Aga Khan was coming from his palace in Poona, rajahs of native states and Government officials were to gather with the whole city to pay tribute to India's beloved healer.

John shook his head as William left for Poona, where it was rumored that the unbelievable was to take place. In honor of the Doctor-sahib, castes and sects were to sit side by side in a great meeting place, and for one evening at least ancient differences were to be forgotten. To residents of India it sounded impossible, but then, when the Doctor-sahib was present, impossible things had a way of taking place.

The Empire Cinema, the largest theatre in Poona, was crammed tight to overflowing. Milling crowds outside fought to gain entrance, but even the aisles were jammed.

Adding further decoration to an already over-decorated platform were the colorful, gleaming garments of the notables. Rulers of native states, religious leaders and high Government officials, many of whom came from hundreds of miles to attend, crowded the stage. Jewels, feathers, flowers, flags, bunting and colored lights blended into a flamboyant background against which the guest of honor stood out with the simplicity of a sheet of paper.

Overhead lights gleamed on the ample expanse of his baldness, running into absorption only at a thin fringe of hair behind his ears. A dark coat, straining at the buttons, encompassed his round, heavy figure.

As had been breathlessly rumored, Mohammedans, Hindus, Parsees, Christians and missionaries melted into a congenial, harmonious unity to pay farewell tribute to the great healer of India . . . the Doctor-sahib with the miracle-hands.

A deep, respectful silence from the great audience attended the words of the Hindu speaker, Mahadev Chaubel, a great Indian and an honored leader. He stood on the platform, spoke in a clear, flute-like voice.

" It was almost forty years ago when you first set foot in our country. Now, in the year 1928, because of your industry, skill and devotion, Miraj has the largest mission medical plant in all India."

William was somewhat embarrassed by this form of address. He had to adjust himself to an almost too personal tribute.

" You began your care of the sick by placing some bottles in a tumbled-down donkey shed . . ."

From his seat on the platform the doctor could look deep into the auditorium, could recognize hundreds of the upraised, glowing faces. He shifted the massive flower garlands laden about his neck, felt the warmth of the friendly shoulder of the Maharajah of Kolhapur seated next to him.

> ". . . Besides Miraj you have founded hospitals in six places: Kodoli, Ashta, Vita, Nipani, Kurli and Kolhapur. They are prospering, day by day."

Although it was thirty years ago it seemed such a short time to William since there had been just Miraj and seven students. But today there were Ashta, Vita, Nipani, Kurli, Kodoli, and Kolhapur, each with its own hospital building, each run by a Miraj graduate. Hundreds of his other medical graduates had gone into private practice or were serving in mission and government hospitals. These young men were the fingers of Miraj. They were the shoots of his own work, boring their roots into Indian soil, spreading the message of healing and good will.

> " . . . During these well-nigh forty years you have treated one million, five hundred thousand people, performed operations on seventy-five thousand, and given sight to thirteen thousand blind."

One million, five hundred thousand patients. William smiled. It sounded so impressive in words. It had seemed so ordinary in deed. Just one day after the other after the other, year in and year out. And thirteen thousand blind. What a thrill it had been to open the eyes of blind men. Of all his work, that had been the most rewarding—restoring sight. He looked down at his hands. They had served him well.

The audience stirred as the great Aga Khan, religious head of the Moslems of India, arose to address the honored guest. He was tall and proud, a figure of dignity and reserve.

> " Of far greater value than even your medical skill has been your Christlike example. It has proved of incalculable value in the regeneration of India, and has, in no small measure, contributed to the hastening of the coming of the Kingdom of God. . . ."

A deep emotion stirred within the doctor. This— from a Mohammedan. " The hastening of the Kingdom." Thank the Lord I didn't compromise and discriminate between castes and sects, he breathed. Because unity is possible. I proved it at Miraj and they've proved it here tonight in this hall.

> ". . . The story of the work in Miraj is one of continued success. One small room in an out-of-the-way street in Miraj has developed into a hospital of fifty buildings."

A hospital of fifty buildings. Well, that had been easy enough. He could scarcely remember a time during the past score of years when the sound of construction was not in his ears. There was the main hospital with fifty buildings, the leper asylum and home for untainted children, the six branch hospitals with their thirty buildings—all had been built with funds donated by the Indian people. And the receipts from the hospital work kept up the institutions, paid all assistants' salaries, and made it unnecessary to send to missionary-minded Americans and Canadians for financial aid. The work was on a self-supporting basis. He cleared his throat, pulled down his coat.

". . . You built a Leprosarium and for thirty-five years have cared for the lepers. And now, in addition to your other excellent work of building, is started a Tuberculosis Sanatorium."

His T. B. San. That had been a hard one. " No, no . . . impossible! " everyone had said two years before. " Where will you build it? Where will you get the funds? " He had been met with more pessimism on that project than any other. " But I showed them," he chuckled to himself, for western India needed a sanatorium and he was determined there should be one. Hand in hand with gradual industrial progress had come tuberculosis. Workers, living in tenement-houses in the large cities, quickly succumbed to the disease. Then the epidemic spread to the people of the village areas. His work would not be complete without a place to care for them. From the hospital receipts he had purchased a tract of 100 acres between the native states of Miraj and Sangli, but it was only after letters, calls, and even a radio broadcast from Bombay that the subscription list was started. One building had gone up. In another six months, with a lot of hard work to raise the necessary money . . . William sighed. He was going home. The others would have to take care of building the T. B. San. Impatience at his failing physical structure irritated the doctor. " I wish I had a body young enough to keep pace with my mind! " he fumed.

". . . Your most fitting memorial is the great Medical Centre which you have built."

Memorial! I wish people wouldn't think of me as dead, he groaned. But then he smiled. This was their way of expressing love and appreciation.

Following the Aga Khan's speech, an address was made by Dr. Nichol MacNichol of the Church of Scotland Mission. A Christian leader was addressing a Mohammedan and Hindu audience. They gave him their full attention.

" This service of yours will prove useful in bringing about a revolution in the thoughts of others, getting people to follow the right way and carrying out the best kind of prescribed work."

William looked into the audience, at the faces of young men and women he knew so well. How different modern India from the India he had first

known. Assurance, curiosity, aggressiveness, a
quickening national pulse, a desire to stand worthily
beside other nations, not as outcasts or heathen
strangers, but as men and women filled with knowledge and light. Because their mothers and grand-
mothers had listened to him, had endured inoculation, cleaned their yards, learned of hygiene and
sanitation, depended upon western knowledge of
childbirth and discarded the ignorant midwife—these
young people were here and healthy. And their eager
eyes penetrated into the future, and their hearts
burned with a desire to serve their country well.
Someday they would be ready—and he would have
helped them prepare.

It was not until the great figure of the Maharajah
lumbered forward to the front of the platform that a
catch came in William's throat, and he felt his eyes
smarting. The organ-low voice, the hulking, kindly
figure filled the doctor with heart-catching memories.
The hunting trip, the wedding carriage, the unexpected gift of a hospital in his city of Kolhapur
which he named Mary Wanless Zenana Hospital, and
then a five-acre tract of land for the building of new
Medical College buildings when the original hospital
compound had become too crowded.

" Because you have poured the handfuls
of the water of your good deeds on the root
of the tree of Christianity that tree has been
fully adorned with branches and blossoms
and its branches have spread through the

land. Your hospital has grown like the sap-
ling banyan that in time becomes a veritable
lord of the forest affording shelter to whole
multitudes under its living colonnades and
cloistered shades."

He had seen a banyan tree the first time he went to
hunt with the Maharajah. Through his mind flashed
the hunting trip when the two of them had sat tense,
waiting for the tiger; other hunting trips through the
years when Lillian had finally permitted their two
sons, Harold and Robert, to enjoy the thrill of a
jungle hunt with the Maharajah. And the Maharajah's first words after his serious stroke of last year,
" It's my right arm. I won't be able to hunt any
more." And he had sobbed like a youngster.

" Our hearts are filled with grief because
you are leaving this land to go to your own
country. . . ."

" My own country," thought William. " This is
my country." He recalled John's warning: " You'll
have to rest." That meant leave India. He and
Lillian would go to America where their two boys
were now in school, where his eldest child, Ethel, lived
with her husband. But John had said, " Why not
stay at Miraj? You have your bungalow. I'll see
that you get the best of care."

But William felt the same way about staying as
Victoria May. He remembered her, five years before,
prim, sailor-hatted head tossed high as she stood on

the station platform, ready to " go home." " I'd only take up room if I stayed here," she said, gulping back her tears. " At Miraj every nurse has more important work than waiting on a failing missionary."

". . . Finally, we take leave of you with the prayer that the Great Savior Physician who has given wonderful success to your work and has made it to be always remembered, bless and keep you."

He turned and looked at William, and sadness shrouded his face. This was farewell. Within the hall was silence. The deep voice was reverent.

". . . May the Lord give you a safe journey over the seas and bring you in happiness and safety to your native land."

His words died out. A sigh, as frail and sad as a dying bird, fluttered through the hall. One stark, silent moment poised in time, while William's brain thundered the word, " Through! "

And yet—his heart said differently. A frivolous, precocious hope pricked at his sadness and made parting unreal. " I'll be back . . . I'll be back," it shrilled, while his mind glowered darkly at this ridiculous nymph which raised impossible hopes.

A brass band shattered the quiet moment. The audience arose. After that there were heaping armfuls of finest, costly gifts; salaams and good words; weeping women and sorrowful children; brave, grateful men; until it seemed to William that he had already died and was at this moment receiving his heavenly reward.

And now it was William's last evening in Miraj. A heavy tropical moon hung in the sky, lighting up the hospital compound with its friendly smile and making a perfect setting for the doctor's final farewell.

A large tent had been pitched near the Anatomical Building. The flaps of the tent were lifted up to let in the moonlight and fresh, cool air. Guests strolled through the compound, chatting softly as the tent gradually filled. In contrast to the previous night's gathering at Poona, there were no state officials here, no glittering jewels or potentates' magnificence. The tent had quietly filled with earnest, unobtrusive men dressed in simple English-cut suits, and women whose lack of ornamentation bespoke their Christian affiliation. There was a home-like atmosphere about this gathering—like children honoring a well-loved father.

As William sat upon the improvised platform he felt like a father to those before him, for they were his medical school graduates, his nurses and compounders—the men and women who now wore his mantle upon their shoulders. They were himself, multiplied over and over, hundreds of times. They had come back to Miraj from over all India—to say good-bye. These were the ones who would carry on.

William reminded himself that he should feel sadness at this occasion, but there was only overwhelming gratitude in his heart because he had been led to train these Indian people—to impart the knowledge of his experience so it would continue to spread and grow. "Suppose I were retiring, taking my skills with me," he thought, then looked with pleasure upon the bright, enlightened faces before him. "When the best attributes of the East and West combine in a person," he said to himself, "you find near-perfection."

The farewell ceremony was simple. These people knew of the doctor's ailment, and though some came for hundreds of miles they asked no more than to shake his hand and speak a word of gratitude.

There were souvenir gifts for the doctor. One, a gold scalpel, symbolized the power he had passed on to his students—symbolized his sharing of self. Among the solid silver oriental scrolls, containing letters of esteem, was one from the Alumni, embossed with a picture of the Medical College and inscribed with the doctor's name as Founder and Principal. Some other scrolls were from the hospital staff, patients and Miraj city. And then came the final surprise. A portrait was being unveiled, and as William looked he gasped—for staring him right in the eye was his own likeness, younger and some leaner, but an excellent likeness in oils.

"Dr. Wanless, we shall place this in the Medical College where it shall continue

A Class of the Medical College

to be an inspiration to students and in memory of your many miraculous achievements
and your unselfish life."

The words were uttered by the chairman of the
evening. There was but one speaker. It was
Anandrao returned for this reunion of old students
who came to bid farewell to Dr. Wanless. Experienced now, and skilful, William's first and most
promising student caused his heart a nostalgic
wrench.

" If some days ago the idea of ever parting from and bidding farewell to you had in
wistful moments crossed our minds fugi-
tively, we should have dismissed it as a somewhat queer freak of fancy; but today the
idea stands not as a possibility, needing an
effort of the imagination to realize, but as
stark fact challenging our inmost feelings."

Anandrao the sober-faced; the frightened, timid
Christian. Anandrao who had become a powerful
leader, a great healer, a man who made William's
heart tug with pride. As clearly as he saw the adoring faces before him, the doctor saw in his mind's eye
a frightened youth whose stolid face was wet with
tears, whose voice had cried out: " The sacrifice! I
cannot make the sacrifice! " And yet he had.

". . . We have only to look about us to see
the material evidence of the mighty works
you have done. But great as these are, they
are overshadowed by that more incalculable

force, your influence upon India and her people. Today you are known all over India, nay the world. It is with pleasure that we here tonight remind ourselves that your influence will continue for long. The graduates of the College you founded, the hundreds of nurses and compounders who have felt your presence and the people of India who have seen Christ in and through you are living, growing witnesses to the power of a life consecrated to Him."

The brown faces in the audience carried in them a passionate fervor for their chosen work. If he, as one man, could accomplish what he had in forty years, what would four hundred trained, dedicated Indian doctors accomplish? "This is my greatest work," William decided. "This is my most worth-while endeavor."

Anandrao closed with the poet's lines:

"Strong souls live like fire-hearted suns,
To spend their strength in farthest action,
Breathe more freely in mighty anguish
Than in trivial ease."

William looked at Anandrao. Tears trembled on the Indian's lids. He had known the desire for trivial ease—and had come to know the strength of mighty anguish, like the doctor whom he loved.

"We shall always remember with gratitude and pride that it was you who trained us. May we ask you to convey to friends wherever you may go, that if anything could help us to form noble ideals and live noble lives, it would be the example of you, Dr. Wanless, and men like you, who interpret to the world God's message of Love.''

There was no applause. Somehow their heads bent in quiet prayer and they found themselves lifted up in a spirit of ecstasy which comes only to those who serve for Love—and Love alone.

18

THE LITTLE engine tugged and strained as it pulled its long tail up over the statuesque Western Ghats. Each car teemed with India's ever-on-the-move population. Red saris, gold jewelry, bright turbans and white dhotis formed changing patterns of color, generously interspersed with brown-skinned turbaned men wearing English-made suits. Babies screamed and mothers fretted, but a group of college men vigorously discussed proposed new irrigation canals; a bearded Indian official balanced a box of lantern-slide pictures on his knees as he anticipated his journey into southern villages where he would show and explain to farmers new methods of agricultural procedure; a young Hindu mother expounded scientific care and feeding of babies to an older woman beside her; two young clerks debated heatedly upon home rule.

" Why are you crying, Mama? " Her daughter's voice caused Lillian to daub her eyes hastily, then turn from the train window toward her ten-year-old Margaret with an apologetic smile.

" I'm just being silly and sentimental," she replied.

" Daddy isn't crying." It was evident the girl was proud of her father's restraint.

Lillian watched William as he sat quietly, staring

at the passing landscape. She touched his hand. "William, don't brood about it."

And then she saw his eyes. There was no hint of brooding. Instead they sparkled with anticipation. Lillian recognized the symptoms.

"William Wanless, what in the world are you planning now?"

The doctor's full face beamed as he removed his topee. "I know where I can get another donation toward the T. B. San."

Lillian fell back in the seat, gasping. "But you've retired! You're going to America! John said you were in no condition to do another lick of work."

The doctor winked at his daughter, who was listening intently to the conversation. "Who said this is work?" He wiped the perspiration from his face and bald head. "Remember that rich grain merchant who came to Miraj? The one I operated on for gastroenterostomy?" Lillian nodded briefly. "If I make a personal call on that man he may give us a substantial donation."

"But he doesn't live in Bombay."

The doctor waved aside his wife's objections. "He lives in Nasik. Just overnight from Bombay. It would be an easy matter for me to drop over there before the boat sails."

Lillian folded her arms helplessly, stared at her human dynamo. "William Wanless, are you ever going to relax? Just once in all your life?"

But the doctor only grinned and went on with his

plans. He would visit Bhaurav Ohol, the grain merchant, while waiting for the boat to America.

Three days later, in the heat of a Bombay afternoon, Lillian frantically paced the room of her hotel.

" He should have been here hours ago." Her voice sounded frayed and tired.

" Why don't we telephone to the Victoria Station again? " Margaret jumped up, anxious to use the brand-new city discovery. But Lillian shook her head.

" We called just five minutes ago." Her apprehension increased. She tapped her fingers nervously. " I should have gone with him." Then tearfully, " If anything's happened to your father . . ." Her voice trailed off. " He should have returned yesterday. The train came in on schedule." She considered calling the police, sending word to John in Miraj. " I just don't know what to do," she moaned, then stopped. Footsteps sounded outside the room.

Lillian flung open the door—and standing in the doorway, with a smile like the curve of a Mohammedan crescent, was William. With a cry she threw herself into his arms.

" You're back! You're back! "

His wife's concern disturbed the doctor. He hadn't anticipated her anxiety.

" Have you been all right? " Her eyes bored into his.

"My dear," he planted a moist kiss on Lillian's cheek, "you shouldn't have worried. I had an excellent interview . . . excellent!" He methodically placed his brief case on a small table, removed and hung up his topee.

"But I expected you back last evening," she quavered, feeling weak with relief.

"Oh." He hesitated, then changing the subject turned to his daughter and tweaked her pigtails. "Well, Margaret, it won't be long before you and your brothers can tease each other again."

"William!"

Lillian's voice brought him back to the previous subject of conversation. "Why did you stay an extra day?" There was something he hadn't told her. Suppose he'd had another heart attack? Maybe he had missed the train back.

"Well," the doctor patted his round stomach, settled back in his chair, "I couldn't see Bhaurav Ohol the day I got into Nasik."

"Oh!" Lillian's relief deflated all her fear. "He wasn't at home then?"

"To tell you the truth, I don't know."

"But ——"

"Now, Lillian, you're going to scold me, I know. But," a twinkle crept into his eye as he held out a bright yellow check, "it was worth it."

Margaret, seeing the check, shrilled out, "How much, Daddy?" but Lillian stopped her.

"I want to hear what your father thinks I'm going

to scold him about," she said, and tried to fortify herself against William's irresistible spirit.

He drew a deep breath. " I arrived there after five o'clock. As you know, no business man in this country will see you on business after five. So I had to wait until morning. At——"

Lillian interrupted. " But where did you spend the night? Is there a hotel in Nasik? "

William paused, rubbed his chin. " No, there isn't."

" Well——"

" I slept in the railroad station." There, he'd told her. He sat back, waiting for her protests.

" In the—in the railroad station? " his wife managed.

He nodded. " I slept on a bench."

" Ohhhh! " She sank into a chair. A hopeless despair fixed its claws into her heart. " William, in your physical condition you ——"

He strode to her side, patted her shoulder. " It didn't hurt me. As a matter of fact, I'm getting too soft. Need a bit of roughing it once in awhile." He walked to the desk, sat down and reached for pen and envelope. " Wait until John sees this check," he chuckled. " It takes more than an upstart heart to put William Wanless out of commission."

As the boat pulled out from the harbor, Bombay gleamed and glistened in the sunlight. Victoria Station, the University Tower, Malabar Hill stood out like farewell gestures. Lillian stared curiously at her husband as they stood at the rail, watching the fading shores of India.

" William, I can't understand it. You don't seem a bit sad about leaving India."

He turned puckish eyes upon her face. " I'm not! "

She was almost indignant. " But after all these years ——"

He lifted a warning finger, smiled into the distance. " Something tells me, Lillian," he lifted his eyebrows into the middle of his forehead, " that this isn't good-bye. I'm going to see India again! "

19

Glendale, Calif.,
June 14, 1928.

Dr. John Holmes,
Miraj Hospital,
Miraj, India.

Dear John:

Why don't you send me word of the T. B. San.?
Are you building any new wards? Are you able to
raise more funds? You've only written about Miraj
and outlying dispensary work. I want to know about
the sanatorium. Is the bungalow that I built before
leaving occupied? Are there any patients? Have
provisions been made for patients?

Lillian, Margaret and the boys send regards. I had
a long visit with Ethel, my eldest child you remember, and she's made me a grandfather! I still want to
know about the T. B. San. Please write details.

Best to you and the staff,

WILLIAM J. WANLESS.

Miraj, India,
Sept. 4, 1928.

Dr. William Wanless,
Glendale, California.

My Dear Doctor:

The reason I haven't written about the T. B. Sanatorium is because there's been nothing to write. We
erected a large cottage to accommodate four patients

348

with the check you sent us from your grain merchant friend, Bhaurav Ohol, but am sorry to say that the donations have slowed down. Raising funds is almost a full-time job in itself (except for a whirlwind like yourself), and we've been so busy doing the everyday work that the plans for the Sanatorium have not worked out as expected.

However, we have no intention of dropping the idea. It's just slower than anticipated.

In case you haven't heard, we received a letter the other day telling us of the death of Victoria May. She was a true Christian character and will go to her well-earned rest. I know that if there is a place among the saints, Victoria May will be there wearing her high-buttoned shoes and straw hat.

That's all for now. I want to read my medical journal and then go to bed. Hope you are well and that the California climate treats you right.

Best wishes from all of us,

JOHN HOLMES.

Glendale, Calif.,
Nov. 1, 1928.

Dr. John Holmes,
Miraj Hospital,
Miraj, India.

Now look here, John.

You didn't answer all my questions about the T. B. San. Is it operating? You said another cottage had been built, but are there any patients? I know you're busy, but I wish you'd give me the satisfaction of a few details in your letters.

Here I am cooped up in a sunny, clean bungalow with the California weather doing its best to cheer me up, and all I do is mope and worry about that

Sanatorium. After India this place is like paradise—no snakes, no lepers, no epidemics, plenty of food, an abundance of good weather. The only trouble is—my heart is back in Miraj.

Let me know the details, John.

Regards from the family to you and the staff.

WILLIAM WANLESS.

P.S. Have you tried to follow up some of my letters to the Parsees in Bombay? They have been very liberal with donations and I feel they would make important contributions to the T. B. San.

W. W.

P.P.S. If you can make a trip to Nasik, why not contact Bhaurav Ohol again and have him introduce you to some of his rich friends. He was very much impressed with our work.

W. W.

P.P.P.S. Dear John: For the sake of the peace-of-mind of the Wanless family will you please write the Doctor a long, long letter about the T. B. Sanatorium? Hopefully,

LILLIAN.

Feb. 28, 1929.
Miraj, India.

Dr. William J. Wanless,
Glendale, California.

Dear Doctor:

In answer to your earnest plea I must make a confession. The plans for the T. B. Sanatorium have been temporarily abandoned. We ran out of funds.

I know what you'll be saying, but you were the only person who could manage to raise enough money to make it a reality. We've tried, but somehow we just don't have the knack—nor the time.

Miraj hospital is crowded to the doors all the time. Every ward is jammed with patients. We're working day and night. There are sixty medical students at the present time. More young men, many University graduates, are making application daily. I don't know where we'll put them all.

There's a sad piece of news I have to tell you in this letter. Your good friend, the Maharajah of Kolhapur, passed away last week very suddenly. I attended him, in fact he sent for me and I stayed at the palace overnight and was with him at the end. I think he sent for me for one reason—to talk about you. As he was dying he handed me a Testament you'd given him years before and asked me to read, which I did.

As you can imagine the royal funeral procession was spectacular, befitting his rank. But somehow his heart seemed more attuned to the simplicity of the Scriptures. His son is reigning now and is a fine, progressive man.

I'm sorry that this letter brings only bad news, but you might as well know the truth about the Sanatorium. If I'd thought you were going to do nothing but worry anyway, I might have let you stay in Miraj to start the whole thing rolling. Well, there's no use in regrets.

Regards to you and the family,

JOHN HOLMES.

Glendale, Calif.,
April 21, 1929.

Dear John:

I have had a complete check-up with my physician, a very excellent physician by the way, and he informs me I am well enough to stand an ocean trip. Even as far as India.

Regards,

WILLIAM WANLESS.

July 1, 1929.
Miraj, India.

Mr. Dear Dr. Wanless:

When I showed your letter to the staff there was no silencing them. I haven't told you, but they've been after me for weeks to send for you. In fact, several state officials have been asking about the progress of the Sanatorium and, very much ashamed, we had to admit our failure. They always ended by saying, " If Dr. Wanless were here he could do it." I have also been deluged by requests from private citizens asking me to send for you—if your health would permit.

So, inasmuch as your attending physician has given his consent, all I can say is God bless you and hurry back home!

Affectionately,

JOHN.

20

William's hands trembled as he steadied himself against the rail of the ship.

"Please, William, don't get too excited." Lillian had promised herself not to worry, but couldn't keep the anxiety from her voice.

"By George," the doctor exclaimed as the ship drew up to the dock in Bombay. "There's a crowd down here today."

And then they caught sight of him. "Doctor-sahib!" "Doctor-sahib!" They shrilled, called, whistled and waved their frantic, eager hands. "Doctor-sahib!" "Wanless-sahib!" Men, women, children and babies—all colors: Hindus, Mohammedans, Parsees, Jains and Englishmen seemed to go wild as they recognized the plump, white-suited figure on deck. A great roar of welcome went up. Bombay stretched out her arms and opened her heart in love to the man who had returned once more. Suddenly William found his eyes wet and his heart thumped with the magic of coming home.

And so it was all down the coast. At every village and at every stop: garlands, flowers, songs and gifts. The people massed about the car and showered him with tokens of their love.

"I thought I knew something of Indian gratitude

when I left," he said, " but this . . ." His voice was husky.

Lillian sighed. " I might as well face it," she said to herself, watching a shouting throng. " If this does prove too much for him, he's happiest this way. And I promise I won't regret that we've come."

As the train neared Miraj station, a group of people lined the tracks. Lillian saw them first. " Who can they be? " she wondered. " Why aren't they meeting us at the station instead of half a mile from it? " And then she knew. Formed on both sides of the railroad tracks, their hands filled with flowers, were the patients of the leper home. Not allowed to mingle with the welcomers at Miraj station, they had come from the colony two miles away and had waited long to give a swift greeting to the doctor who had shown them Christian love.

" Doctor-sahib! "

Shrill voices raised in a frantic ovation while emaciated arms and hands waved a swift greeting to the doctor who was as a father to them. As the train passed them, William leaned from the window and called out warm personal greetings, for he recognized them all.

As he settled back in his chair Lillian noticed that the welcome of the lepers had touched William more deeply than any other reception.

At Miraj, as at other stations, there was a tumultuous welcome attended by hundreds. Back at the hospital John begged William to rest. But the doctor

laughed. " I never felt better," he crowed. " Can't
put me to bed like an old man." And much to John's
chagrin William sat up late into the night, making
plans and talking over ideas for the tuberculosis sanatorium.

The next day he went to work.

To Bombay, to Belgaum, to Calcutta, to Benares,
to every part of India, William's letters flew like
released birds, descending over the country in a
white shower.

To grain merchants, money-lenders, wealthy
widows, churches, newspapers, rajahs, maharajahs
and chiefs of native states, to political leaders, government officials, ex-patients and friends of ex-
patients the white missals made their way.

Detailed plans for the proposed buildings were
drawn up, their exact location on the 100 acres indicated. Administration building, laboratory, chapel,
physician's bungalow, ground plant with special
wards, ten one-patient cottages, four two-patient cottages, a well, a powerhouse, servants' quarters, the
large building of special wards, nurses' cottage,
Indian doctor's bungalow, kitchen, nursing superintendent's house and even a badminton court and
tennis court were planned.

A policy was formulated, basis of organization
laid. With patient, painstaking care William
worked out every detail. He had a complete prospec-
tus printed and distributed throughout India, he
traveled from place to place, speaking, contacting

friends, contacting prospects. He followed up letters and correspondence with personal calls. His days and nights were filled, and the money started to come in.

Firm, definite leadership, careful planning, an inspired leader—these were the needed ingredients for the building of the tuberculosis sanatorium. And these William supplied.

" Your husband's having the time of his life," observed John as he and Lillian made a careful record of incoming contributions for the sanatorium.

" I'm so afraid he'll overdo it. He never thinks of saving himself." Tears welled in Lillian's blue eyes.

John nodded. " And yet you wouldn't want him to be inactive."

She hastily dried her eyes. " I know. It's just that it's not easy to share him . . . especially now, when every moment . . ." She bit her lips; spoke hastily in a changed voice.

" Er—here's a donation from a Parsee lady."

John dipped his pen in the inkwell. " How much? "

" Mrs. Jamsetji, rupees twenty thousand."

" Say, that's a good amount," John mentioned as he entered more figures neatly in the rapidly-growing column.

Mrs. J. S.	20,000
Mr. G. K. D.	5,000
The Tata Charities	25,000

Lillian's hair shone silvery-grey in the lamplight. "And here is a check from Praja Nagarwalla. She hasn't much herself, but some years ago William saved her brother. So, when she learned that William had returned to India to raise funds, Miss Nagarwalla took a petition to Parsees and officials in Poona and raised this money herself." Lillian laid aside the papers. "She told William she'd only started. She expects to raise ten thousand rupees before she is through."

John nodded. "These Indian people would give their lives for your husband." His face became grave. "And so would I."

The chugging of an automobile stopping in the compound announced William's return.

"Thank goodness, he's back early," his wife exclaimed, glancing at her watch.

John's face had grown grim. "Earlier than I'd expected," he said and started toward the door. He was stopped by the entrance of William, leaning on the arm of his youthful motor-walla.

Lillian's face paled. "William, what happened?"

But William only smiled as he was helped into a chair. "Nothing." His breathing was labored. Beads of perspiration dotted his forehead. "If you'll leave me with John a minute, my dear," he managed, then added, "Don't worry. I'm fit as a buffalo."

Lillian started to protest, but at John's nodded

request she slipped from the room as did the motor-walla.

William leaned back and grinned apologetically. "She's cutting up again, John," and he pressed his hand to his heart.

John made no reply as he set about to prepare a sedative, but the muscles worked in his cheek.

"It's nothing serious." William seemed over-anxious to reassure him, but the younger man was silent.

"Come, man!" the aged doctor boomed. "Say what's on your mind! Don't keep it to yourself." He chuckled, "It may have unpleasant effects upon your liver."

But John was in no mood for jollity. A deep furrow creased his forehead. "You know what I'm thinking." He pressed a glass upon the doctor. "Here, drink this."

William gulped down the liquid, placed the glass upon the floor with gusto. "Good as new!" he boomed and started to get up. But John motioned him back into the chair.

"Now look here," and the furrow deepened, breaking into worried wrinkles, "you've got to make a decision."

William waved his plump hand as though to dismiss the subject. "Let me tell you about the meeting tonight." But he was stopped by the sharpness in the other's voice.

"Let's talk about your condition!"

This suggestion was greeted with a sigh of impatience.

" That's irrelevant and immaterial and I refuse to discuss it. Now, about that meeting."

But John was not to be sidetracked. Approaching the older man he stood over him, hands in his pockets, his eyes worried and apprehensive. " Dr. Wanless," the voice was grave, " if you don't slow down you're going to drop in your tracks one of these days." The older man lowered his head. The voice continued. " I want you to go home."

Silence reigned. William lifted a heavy hand to his forehead, wiped away the perspiration. John began to pace the floor. " I know how you feel about leaving this place. You built it up, carried on the work these forty years training Christian leaders, caring for the lepers, diagnosing for a million sick people, performing thousands of successful operations and snatching patients from the grave." He paused a second for breath, then hastily resumed. " Why, man alive, if you had done those cataract operations only, giving sight to 13,000 blind, that in itself would have been a lifetime work for one man! Isn't it time you took a rest ? "

William continued to stare at his feet. " Your influence in extending the Kingdom has reached far and wide. Haven't you done enough for India ? " The pacing stopped. John faced the doctor. " What about it ? "

Without raising his eyes William spoke and his

voice was dogged with persistence. "I've got to start that tuberculosis sanatorium. It's got to be done!"

"But you're not well enough!"

William rose from his chair, stood with shoulders squared and his voice was sure and calm. "I intend to open the sanatorium," he said positively. Then the familiar twinkle came into his eyes. "After that, if I'm still alive, I'll follow your advice and go home."

He patted the younger doctor on the shoulder, opened the door and went out onto the verandah to join Lillian.

Six weeks passed, and then William said, "I think it's time to start building." So work started immediately.

Over the rough land patient oxen dragged stones, lumber and building supplies as crews of brown workmen scurried about with hammers, trowels, nails and flints in their hands laying the foundations, preparing for continued action.

Five months passed, a large building with airy wards was completed near the doctor's bungalow and cottage.

"John," William said to his assistant, "I've a surprise for you today."

John looked curiously at William. "What is it this time?"

The older doctor's eyes twinkled brightly as he told

of the physician and nurse he had placed in the new
T. B. Sanatorium. The younger man sat up straight.

" You did! "

" Not only that," William enjoyed the other's surprise, " but I admitted my first patient this morning."

John shook his head. He had never been able to
catch up with the indefatigable Dr. Wanless and he
never would.

That afternoon a quiet celebration was held. Members of the staff, the new doctor, and nurse, the new
patient, Lillian and William rejoiced together as he
proclaimed the Tuberculosis Sanatorium a thriving,
living unit of the hospital work.

It was in the middle of the sixth month that
William spoke seriously to John. He had spent the
morning at the Sanatorium but in the afternoon, returning to the hospital, a terrifying weariness had
seized him.

" John," he said, " I'm going back to America."
He thrust his hands deep into his pockets. " The
building of the San. has been started, you've a doctor,
nurse, and enough donations to keep things going for
a long time. It will continue to grow now under its
own power."

Suddenly William felt very tired. He knew that
his work was finished.

John nodded slowly, considering his next words.
" The people will want to plan some great farewell

celebrations, I know." Here a warning flashed in his face. "Will you take my advice just this once and slip away quietly?"

To his surprise, William agreed. "I think I'd better." And for the first time the older doctor napped for two hours in the middle of the afternoon.

From a sudden flurry of dust in the compound came a voice. "Dr. Wanless! Dr. Wanless!" As the figure drew near the doctor's bungalow, John could see the clerk, Gorderao, frantically beckoning and waving a piece of paper.

John hurried to the edge of the verandah. "Gorderao, I must ask consideration for the doctor. He's taking a nap. If there's hospital business I'll take care of it."

But Gorderao, for the first time in his history as hospital clerk, ignored a rebuff. Lowering his voice which was vibrant with excitement he continued to wave the piece of paper in the air.

"Dr. Wanless," he gasped. "For Dr. Wanless!"

"This is no time to bother the doctor," scolded John.

Gorderao gulped in his excitement, spluttered a few words then frantically pressed the opened telegram into John's hand.

John read—then his eyes flew open wide and he shouted at the top of his lungs.

"William! Oh, William!" He dashed into the bungalow and awakened the sleeping doctor.

GEORGE THE FIFTH BY THE GRACE OF GOD

of GREAT BRITAIN IRELAND AND THE BRITISH
DOMINIONS BEYOND THE SEAS KING DEFENDER OF THE FAITH

To all to whom these Presents shall come Greeting Know Ye that We of Our especial grace certain
knowledge and mere motion have given and granted and by these Presents do give and grant unto
Our trusty and well-beloved WILLIAM JAMES WANLESS Esquire the degree title honour
and dignity of a KNIGHT BACHELOR together with all rights precedences privileges and
advantages to the same degree title honour and dignity belonging or appertaining In Witness
whereof We have caused these Our Letters to be made Patent Witness Ourself at Westminster
the fifth day of March in the eighteenth year of Our Reign.

By Warrant under The King's Sign Manual.

Schuster.

LETTERS PATENT.

" What is it ? " yawned William.

Trembling, John pressed the telegram into his hands. " Look what came for you," he shouted, then in his excitement read aloud over William's shoulder.

" As Editor of The Bombay Times the news has come to me via Reuters cable from London that George the Fifth, King of England and Emperor of India, has seen fit to bestow upon you the honor of Knighthood. May I add my congratulations and best wishes to those of all India, and say that no other subject has been more worthy of this distinction than our own Sir William James Wanless."

Gorderao had sped like a carrier pigeon over the compound, calling out the news. Instantly the message flew through the hospital, the word jumped from one to another until the whole building was buzzing with excitement. Eager friends crowded about the bungalow, pressing forward against John's protests.

But it was like trying to quell a brush fire. He admitted a few while the others milled about the verandah, calling through the window and crying out the news like joyous children.

Lillian saw the crowd from across the compound and a deadly fear gripped her heart. What had happened to William? Running as fast as possible, she breathlessly covered the ground, ran up the steps and into the bungalow.

Before she could say a word John had grasped her by the shoulders.

" He's a Knight," he exulted. " Sir William, no less! "

" What? " Lillian thought he had lost his mind.

William, in the center of a congratulatory group, stood humbly silent, having stuffed the telegram in his pocket.

Lillian sank quickly into a chair. " Sir William James Wanless " by decree of the King of England and Emperor of India!

That very afternoon letters and telegrams started to arrive. It seemed as if everyone in India wanted to congratulate the doctor. The Viceroy, prominent government officials, rajahs, influential Hindus, Parsees, and people of every class heaped their messages upon him. He was not rejoicing alone. All India was rejoicing with him.

Because her people had not been advised of the doctor's departure, and because he was preparing to leave without ceremony or celebration, the gracious Indian morning rose early and decked herself in her loveliest garments. A flawless blue sky arched high and tucked itself neatly around the edges behind distant earth-brown horizons. Birds twittered and soared into air as fresh as a bubbling well. Tilled fields trembled with the coming of the crops, bullocks stirred lazily waiting for the yoke of the cumbersome carts.

Into this morning rode Sir William, his last, final morning in Miraj. As the comfortable motor car sped along the road to the station he stared out of the back window, filling, cramming his eyes full of the beloved pure whiteness of Miraj hospital. It diminished so quickly. The car traveled so fast. And this time there was no sprightly ray of hope—no promise of return. Miraj. The dearly beloved magic of Miraj. And now it was pinpoints in the distance. He leaned far out of the car. Miraj . . . good-bye . . . good-bye.

Tears flowed down John's face. Lillian sat quietly, her hands clasped tightly together. And all the while the doctor stared and strained toward the far distance where his life had been lived.

The car stopped at the station. Lillian leaned over, touched her husband's arm. "We're here, William."

As he climbed heavily from the car, with a rush of feeling he saw the crowded platform, the smiling, tear-stained faces of those who loved him, and whom he loved. There was no shouting or pushing; all knew of the Doctor-sahib's condition. But they had come to say farewell.

Their considerate quiet touched the doctor most of all. One by one they pressed his hand, murmured softly, or else looked deep into his eyes, saying no words but conveying a message of lifelong gratitude and love. His neck was heavy with their fragrant garlands, and the flower petals twinkled with their tears.

" Here comes our train." Sir William's low voice sounded the warning. Up the track puffed the Bombay Express, conscientiously pounding the same beat year in and year out, distributing, sorting, moving the ever-traveling population of India.

" Well . . ." John held out his hand. The train whistle sounded. A tiny whisper ran through the crowd as the train puffed in and stopped at the platform. Sir William shook hands with John, waved to the crowd, then he and Lillian silently went on board.

A long whistle blew, wheels scraped merrily against steel rails, and with a tug and a chug the Bombay Express was on its clattering way.

John watched for a long time as the busy little train faded farther and farther into the future; waited until everyone else had gone and he was alone on the platform. At last he turned, got into the car and headed it back in the direction of the hospital. There was a busy day ahead. At Miraj—every day was a busy day.